'Like you? You must be joking. Why, I've as much chance of making friends with a rattlesnake as I have with you. There's no way I'm going to end up liking you.'

'No? Well, we'll see, I suppose, but somehow I've got the strangest feeling you might change your mind.'

'Never!' she said hotly, starting up the engine with a mighty roar.

'Never is a long time, honey—a very long time, so how can you be so certain?'

'I am certain, absolutely and totally certain. I wouldn't like you if you were the last man on earth.'

'Well, as I said, we'll soon see,' he said easily, settling back in his seat. 'But do you know, there's just one thing I can't resist?'

'What's that?' she snapped, pulling back on to the roadway. 'Terrorising women?'

He chuckled softly, his green eyes gleaming in swift appreciation of the barb. 'A challenge, Harriet, honey, that's what. And it seems to me you've just thrown down the gauntlet.'

UNEXPECTED CHALLENGE

BY

JENNIFER TAYLOR

MILLS & BOON LIMITED
ETON HOUSE   18-24 PARADISE ROAD
RICHMOND   SURREY   TW9 1SR

*First published in Great Britain 1989
by Mills & Boon Limited*

© Jennifer Taylor 1989

*Australian copyright 1989
Philippine copyright 1989
This edition 1989*

ISBN 0 263 76306 4

*Set in Times Roman 10 on 12 pt.
01-8905-54583 C*

Made and printed in Great Britain

CHAPTER ONE

WITH a snarl and a slam, Harriet closed the bonnet of the car, aiming a quick kick at the front tyre for good measure. Easing a crumpled tissue from the pocket of her tight jeans, she scrubbed hard at the grease stains covering her fingers. Turning, she fixed the buttercup-yellow car with a steely glare.

'It's the last time—do you hear me, Betsy?—absolutely the last time I give you a respray if this is how you pay me back. Now you've got one more chance, just one, to redeem yourself.'

Moving quickly, she slid behind the wheel of the ancient and usually much-loved Morris Traveller and pulled out the choke. Raising her eyes heavenwards, she muttered a short, fervent prayer before turning the ignition. Nothing...not a cough, not a splutter, not even a whimper. St Christopher must be out for the day!

Leaning forwards, she rested her head against the worn wooden curve of the steering wheel, closing her eyes in despair. What on earth could she do? She'd promised to collect Jill at seven and it was gone six-thirty now; far too late to make any other arrangements. Thoughts spun fast as sugar through her brain, but not one of them gave her the answer and she groaned aloud; Jill would kill her if she was late!

A sudden blood-curdling scream rent the air, and with a gasp Harriet shot bolt upright, clasping a hand to her pounding heart to steady its pace. The sound came again and she swivelled round, eyes shooting towards the high stone wall which separated her garden from the one next door.

Two furry forms, one grey, one brown, were locked together on its narrow summit, spitting and scratching in a show of feline fury, and with a curse she leapt from the car and ran towards them.

'Caspar, stop it!' she roared, but it was wasted breath. At five years old and a near stone in weight, Caspar was king of the neighbourhood cats, and determined to keep his title. There was just no way he was going to refuse a challenge from an underling, even at Harriet's request.

Lessening the distance to a mere six yards, Harriet panted to a halt and slipped off her shoe. Balancing it delicately in one hand, she took careful aim, then hurled it towards the fighting cats, eyes widening in horror as it missed its target and sailed straight over the garden wall.

With one last swipe, Caspar sent his opponent packing and, jumping down, strolled victoriously towards her, altering course as he sensed her displeasure. With a twitch of his thick grey tail he entered the shrubbery, obviously deciding not to risk another of his nine lives just at present.

'Bully!' she yelled after his departing form, then with an awkward hobble crossed the last few yards to the wall, wincing as the gravel cut into her bare toes. Easing her one shod foot into a narrow crack in the grey stone she levered herself upwards, clinging grimly to the mossy top while she looked round for the shoe, before finally spotting it resting against the rear wheel of Ken's taxi. About to jump down, she paused as a sudden glorious thought struck her, and an expression of relief crossed the smooth oval of her face as she realised she might just have found the solution to all her problems.

*   *   *

The taxi jerked to a kangaroo halt, and Harriet swore softly as she set the handbrake. Old and temperamental Betsy might be, but driving her was a doddle compared to this great beast. Still, it had served its purpose, and there was more than a hint of relief to her voice when she spoke.

'Right, we've made it, and with a few minutes to spare, after all.' She faced the pair seated in the back, the rather pale cast to their faces giving her a brief moment's concern.

'Hey, are you all right?' she asked anxiously, pushing a stray wisp of curly auburn hair from out of her eyes. 'You're not worried about the flight, are you?'

Running a hand over his damp face, her brother-in-law cast her a baleful glance before replying. 'It's not the flight we're worried about, it's your...'

An elbow caught him sharply in the ribs, cutting off the sentence in mid-flow. Pinning a smile to her shaking lips, Jill faced her sister and finished it for him.

'What Dave is trying to say, Harry, is that we're worried about you. Are you quite sure you don't mind taking over for me? It's such a lot to ask of you.'

Harriet smiled warmly back, ignoring the fact that she'd understood Dave's meaning only too well! In truth, she couldn't blame him for what he'd started to say; it had been years since she'd driven any car other than Betsy and it showed, but it was so typical of Jill to want to spare her feelings.

'Of course I don't mind, in fact I'm quite looking forward to it,' she lied, with as much conviction as she could muster, knowing her sister was quite capable of refusing to go even at this late stage if she suspected otherwise.

'Are you sure?' Still troubled, Jill gazed at her, searching for any hint of doubt, and hastily Harriet looked away.

'Absolutely! Now, come on, both of you, if you don't get checked in pretty soon then you'll miss your flight and that wonderful holiday you've won.'

Smiling, she climbed out of the car, pushing the faint hint of unease to the back of her mind. She'd cope, she'd have to...it was too late to back out now!

Half an hour later the silver plane hurtled skywards, and with a lonely sigh Harriet turned away, hunching her shoulders against the driving rain and glad that she'd seen fit to borrow Ken's jacket as well as his cab. For a brief moment guilt washed through her, but briskly she pushed it aside. There had been nothing else she could have done, given the circumstances, except borrow the taxi, or they would have missed their flight. After all, hadn't Ken asked her to start up the engine while he was away to save the battery from going flat? Surely it was just a small step on from that to give the car this run to the airport.

The rain was coming down in silver sheets now, soaking her head and trickling down her neck; feeling in the pockets of the overlarge coat, she dug out Ken's battered peak cap. Quickly she pulled it on, tucking the straggling damp wisps of rich auburn hair inside before settling the peak low over her eyes as a shield against the cold drops. At a splashing run she covered the last few yards to the car and, wrenching open the unlocked door, slid thankfully inside out of the deluge.

Shivering, she ran a slim hand over her wet face, scooping off water and flicking it aside while her thoughts went to Jill and Dave heading off for two glorious sun-drenched weeks in the Bahamas, and a faint tinge of envy assailed her before she swiftly brought it under control. If there was anyone who deserved a good holiday, it was that pair; years of getting a home together, not to mention bringing up their nine-year-old son Danny, had left little cash over for holidays. Winning this trip was the best thing that could have happened for them.

Harriet slid the key into the ignition, starting the engine with an over-revved roar and grimacing at the sudden flare of noise. She set the car into gear, automatically checking the rear-view mirror before pulling out, her eyes widening with shock as she caught sight of the man slouched in the back. For one heart-stopping moment she froze, stills from every horror movie she'd ever seen where mad rapists and murderers reared up from back seats to attack the poor defenceless driver, flicking across her vision. The blood pounded in her ears, a cold chill enveloped her, and for one dreadful moment she thought she would faint from sheer terror.

'Five Green Lees Lane, please.'

His voice was low, deep and infinitely pleasant with its faint hint of an American accent, and brought her up short. Surely murderers didn't usually offer their address before they struck down a victim, did they? Swallowing hard, she ran her eyes over the hard, tanned planes of his face, taking swift stock of the strong jaw covered with a day's growth of stubble, the green eyes shadowed and dull from lack of sleep. He didn't look like a murderer...he looked far too tired!

Blond hair fell carelessly over a wide brow, and with an impatient gesture he swept it aside, turning fractionally so that their eyes met in the mirror.

'Well?'

There was a curt note to his voice now, and hastily Harriet tried to get herself in hand.

'I'm sorry...' she began.

'Don't tell me you're booked.'

A definite tinge of anger threaded his tone, and she started nervously, more puzzled than ever. What on earth was he on about? In fact, what on earth was he doing in the car if he wasn't planning the unspeakable deeds she'd first imagined? The first trickle of anger started to flow through her, firming her shaking limbs and giving her the courage to question him.

'What are you talking about?' There was a cold note to her voice now, a curtness which almost matched his.

'This is a cab, isn't it?' he demanded abruptly, and Harriet paused.

It was a tricky question, with a yes and no answer, but at least it explained why he was here. He'd obviously seen the taxi plates and thought it was for hire, but now the real question was just how could she get rid of him without causing a scene? She had the feeling the answer might not be that easy.

Swivelling round, she faced him across the back of the seat, brown eyes sweeping over the pale, rather crumpled linen suit he wore with such casual grace, before running up to the taut, compressed line of his mouth, and a shiver of unease crept down her spine. He looked in no mood to be reasonable, to accept explanations, but she had to try. Taking a deep breath, she started to speak, her voice cool and carefully level.

'Yes, of course it's a taxi, but...'

'Well, thank heavens we've agreed on that point!' Levering himself up straighter in the soft leather seat, he stared back at her, obviously making an effort to control his irritation as he continued, 'Look, kid, I didn't mean to snap, but I've been up all night and I'm out on my feet. I'm sorry about getting into the cab while you were away, but frankly there seemed little point in hanging round outside getting soaked. Lord knows where all the other cabs have got to this morning, but so far yours has been the only one to show up. Now, all I want is to get to this address, and as soon as I can.'

Leaning forwards, he thrust a small slip of paper into Harriet's unwilling fingers, raising a dark, quizzical eyebrow when she failed to react.

'Well?'

With a gulp, she dropped her eyes to the paper, staring blindly down at the curling black letters swimming like tadpoles across the white scrap, her mind in a spin. The situation was fast getting out of hand, and she had to do something... but what?

'How about it, then?'

She looked helplessly back at the hard-faced stranger.

'How about what?' she queried, quite missing his meaning.

'The address, do you know where it is, son?' Slowly, carefully, he enunciated every word, evidently unable to believe anyone could be so dumb and, face flaming, Harriet snatched another look at the paper, fast realising the address was a bare ten minutes' drive from her home.

'Yes, I know it,' she snapped back, brown eyes sparking in the pale oval of her face. Irritation speared through her as she remembered his tone; how dared he treat her like a half-wit when it was he... All of a sudden the full impact of his words hit her with a reeling punch. *'Son!'* He'd called her 'son'. Good heavens, he thought she was a boy!

Swiftly she twisted round, casting an astonished glance in the small mirror, and quickly bit back the chuckle of mirth as she caught sight of her reflection. With the collar of the bulky coat turned up and the peak of the cap pulled low, it was easy to see how he could make such a mistake. Right at this moment she was no one's idea of true femininity.

'Well, then, is it too much to ask you to take me there?'

The weary tone cut through her self-absorbed study and Harriet brought her thoughts back to the moment, trying to decide just what she should do. If she tried to explain the mistake and asked him to leave the cab, then she had the nasty suspicion he might cause a scene. But did she really need to? After all, her main worry, the fear of being attacked, seemed groundless now she'd been miscast as a boy. Taking him home could be the easiest way out.

With a low murmur of assent she revved up the engine, her eyes flicking fractionally to the tall figure slumped in the back, and she grinned. It looked as if she'd just got her first fare, didn't it!

With a sigh of relief Harriet eased the car to a halt, resting her head wearily against the hard curve of the steering wheel for a few brief seconds while she caught her breath. If she'd thought the drive to the airport had been bad, then she'd had no idea what the drive back would be like. Crossing the city during the morning rush-hour was guaranteed to give anyone but the most intrepid driver a cardiac arrest, and she thanked heaven for the fact that it would probably be several more years before she had to face it again.

The soft rolling sound of a contented snore echoed from the back seat, and she sent a swift look at the figure sprawled in the back, a faint flicker of annoyance running through her. While she'd been risking life and limb, not to mention her sanity, he'd been happily sleeping ... but not for much longer.

Stepping out of the car, she walked briskly round to the back door and flung it open, letting a nasty blast of chilly air flow cruelly over his comfortable form, but it had little effect. Obviously it would need more than a mere breeze to rouse Sleeping Beauty from his slumbers. Leaning inside, she rested her hand against the tight-packed muscles of his shoulder and shook him hard, stopping immediately she saw the heavy lids flicker open.

'We're there,' she informed him in her most rousing tone. Stepping back, she gave him some room to get out, watching with a sad lack of sympathy as he eased the cramped muscles of his stiffened neck. Standing, he was even taller than she'd imagined, tall and well muscled, and just for a moment she half regretted her masquerade, wishing she'd been dressed in something a little more fetching than the old worn jeans and borrowed cap and jacket. But still, it was probably for the best, all things considered.

'How much, kid?'

Flicking her a brief glance, the man reached inside his jacket and stopped. Quickly he patted his hands over his other pockets, and a sudden spasm of fury contorted his face.

'OK, kid, where is it?' he demanded harshly, and Harriet paused, hand outstretched to close the car door. What did he mean? She opened her mouth to ask him when suddenly a large tanned hand shot out, grasping her wrist in a vicelike grip. She yelped in startled alarm.

'I said, where is it?'

His voice was a low growl, and for a second terror tingled up her spine. Dumbly she stared up into his icy green eyes, then she swallowed hard and forced herself to speak.

'I don't know what you're talking about. Let me go!'

There was a shrill, almost hysterical note to her voice, and for an instant he paused, as though something about the tone had flicked at his mind, but quickly he pushed it aside. He thrust his face a scant six inches from hers, holding her fast as she tried to retreat.

'Listen, kid, the last guy who tried to lift my wallet ended up with a broken arm for his efforts, so get wise, hand it back and spare yourself some pain.'

Slowly he twisted her arm further back, and Harriet felt the swift sting of tears at the back of her eyes.

'I haven't got your damned wallet,' she managed to choke out, but it was difficult to talk through the pain.

'No? Well, we'll soon see about that!'

With a swift movement he spun her round, pushing her forwards so that her arms splayed across the roof of the car. Then, thrusting a foot forward, he kicked her legs apart.

'Let me go!' she cried, fear racing through her. She looked desperately along the empty road, praying that someone would come.

'Not till I've got my wallet back.'

He ran his hands up the length of her legs, and Harriet froze at his touch. This couldn't be happening, it just couldn't, not here in this road full of houses, a mere ten minutes away from home. She had to be dreaming. However, there was nothing dreamlike about the rough touch of his hard hands, and she back-heeled a kick at his shin, having the satisfaction of feeling it connect against bone.

'Cut it out if you know what's good for you, kid.'

Roughly he pushed her further forwards, so that she was forced to half lie over the car, then with one quick wrench he dragged the front of the heavy coat open, tearing off several of the big leather buttons. He patted harshly down the sides of her body, pausing with a swift intake of breath as his fingers encountered the soft, unmistakable swell of her breasts, and for a brief moment everything seemed to stand still.

'What the hell...'

Grabbing her shoulder, he swung her round, his eyes sliding down her from head to toe as she faced him squarely, a faint bloom of colour edging the soft curve of her cheeks.

'You're a girl!'

The look of stunned dismay on his face was so comical that under other circumstances Harriet would have burst out laughing. But not right now. Right now fury was riptiding through her in monumental waves, washing all terror and caution aside. How dared he manhandle her like that? She'd never been so embarrassed or insulted in the whole of her life.

Stepping forwards, she raised her arm, catching his cheek with a stinging blow, feeling the rough rasp of stubble cut into her fingers.

'Why, you...'

He caught her roughly by the shoulders, a murderous set to his face, and for an instant Harriet felt real terror run through her.

'Hey, Harry, what're you doing here? Did you want me for something?'

The boyish voice cut through the tension, and with a sigh of relief Harriet skimmed a look sideways, eyes widening in surprise as she recognised her young nephew Danny racing along the road.

For a brief moment longer the man still held her, hard fingers biting into the slender bones of her shoulders before reluctantly he let her go, and hastily she set several paces between them before turning towards the boy, her whole body trembling with reaction.

'Hi, Danny. Never mind what *I'm* doing, what are *you* doing here?'

It took a lot of effort to keep her tone cool and level, but there was no way she wanted to frighten the child or put him in any sort of danger. Though the man was standing quietly enough now, there was no knowing just what might happen if she allowed the situation to flare up again. Deep down she had the feeling that the only safe way to deal with lunatics was to try and keep things as calm as possible.

Slithering to a halt, Danny stood gasping at her side, his eyes running curiously over the man before he replied to her question.

'I'm staying here, of course, at Mike's house. Surely Mum must have told you?' Hitching a thumb backwards, he indicated the modern stone house she was parked in front of.

'Yes, of course she told me. I ... I just didn't realise this was where he lived. I've not had time yet to look at the paper she gave me with all the details.'

Staring past him, she let her eyes run over the polished-wood door to the gleaming brass number screwed to its top, her mind in a spin. Number five. It was the right number, all right, so just what was going on? How come this maniac had asked her to take him to the very house where Danny was staying? She had to find out. She started to ask him when Danny stepped forwards, holding his hand out to the man who was standing silently watching.

'Hi, you must be Rick. Mike said you'd be coming today. I'm Danny.'

The man took a step forwards and Harriet had to force herself to stand still, every instinct screaming at her to snatch up her nephew and get as far away from this lunatic as possible. With wary eyes she watched as he shook Danny's hand before turning his gaze back to her, and instinctively she stood up a touch straighter, determined he shouldn't see just how much he had scared her.

'Do you know,' he said, his voice low and easy, a mile removed from its previous growl, 'I've the strongest feeling that I've made some sort of terrible mistake.'

CHAPTER TWO

CLOSING THE DOOR, Harriet leant back against the solid support it offered, every tiny bit of her body weak from exhaustion. It was barely eight-thirty in the morning, yet she felt as though she'd just gone ten rounds with Mohammed Ali! She shut her eyes and let the whole of the last unbelievable hour race through her brain in a series of brilliant Technicolor freeze-frames, and felt the colour race under her skin at the memory of how it had felt to have that damnable man touch her!

Fury poured through her veins, straightening her sagging limbs, and with a low, muttered snarl she pushed away from the door and strode briskly through to the kitchen. How dared he? How dared he treat her like that—accuse her of theft, then manhandle her that way? It might be how things were done where he came from, but not here. A whole host of choice comments flooded into her brain and she groaned. What use were all the smart answers now, all the snappy, cutting little comments? She could have done with them ten minutes earlier, when she'd stood dumbly in front of him, unable to think of one single thing to say. Oh, if only she could have a second chance, there'd be nothing dumb about her then!

The telephone rang, its strident tone cutting across the silence in the kitchen and, snatching up the receiver, she snapped crossly, 'Harriet Prince speaking.'

There was a moment's pause, a tiny heartbeat of silent time, as though her sharp response had startled the caller, then a low voice said, 'Miss Prince...Rick Dawson here.'

And Harriet felt herself begin to tremble as she recognised the soft-accented tones. Someone up there must be listening after all, and had heard her plea for a second chance to tell this obnoxious man just what she thought of him! Sucking in a huge breath of air, Harriet prepared to let rip, but he beat her to it, speaking quickly as though anticipating her reaction.

'Listen, Miss Prince, I'm sorry, really sorry about what happened before. I...well, I guess I'm just so used to seeing the seedy side of things that I jumped to all the wrong conclusions.'

There was no doubting the sincerity in his deep voice, and Harriet felt a tiny ripple of regret curl through her as she heard it. She would have so loved to tell him just what sort of a louse he was, but now she couldn't; now politeness dictated that she accept his apology, at least on the surface. Deep down she knew she would never forget the indignity of the situation he'd put her in, would never forget the feel of his hard hands running over her body.

'Miss Prince?'

'I'm still here, Mr Dawson,' she answered crisply. 'I accept your apology.'

'And...?'

'And nothing, Mr Dawson. Look, you made a mistake, a big one, and you've apologised for it, so that, as far as I can see, is the end of the matter.'

'But you're still mad?'

'Too damn right I'm still mad. You frightened the life out of me back there.'

'I know, I'm sorry. Look, is there any way I can see you again, take you out to dinner as a peace off——'

'No...thank you. As I said, just forget it ever happened. Let's face it, you wouldn't even recognise me again if you saw me; I don't usually go round dressed like a boy. It was all one big mistake from start to finish,' she replied flatly.

'Oh, you're wrong there. I'd recognise you, all right, especially if I could rely on touch. You have an unforgettable body, Miss Prince, and my fingers are still tingling with the imprint of it.'

The audacity of the words stole her breath away, so that for a moment she could only stand gaping at the receiver. How dared he? The man was impossible!

'I guess I just blew it again, didn't I?'

The low voice held more than a trace of laughter in its tones and desperately Harriet fought for a measure of calm before she answered coldly, every perfectly enunciated syllable frosted with ice.

'You guessed right. Goodbye, Mr Dawson. I can't honestly say it's been a pleasure meeting you, but it has definitely been an experience; one I have no wish to repeat!'

Carefully, delicately, she replaced the receiver with a soft, gentle click, breathing in deeply, determined to make the veneer of calm stick. There was no way she was going to let him upset her again, no way at all ... he just wasn't worth it! Fists clenched, face set, she counted to ten then stepped back from the phone, stumbling slightly as her heel caught against the soft bundle of fur parked just behind her. She viewed Caspar with a baleful eye, ignoring the series of ingratiating purrs he was uttering.

'So you're back, are you? Well, don't think I've forgotten about this morning. You're not off the hook yet, you bully!'

Hearing the gruff tone to her voice Caspar stood up, puffing out his fur before crossing the room to settle himself on to the cushioned seat of the rocker, every whisker twitching with offended dignity. Curling himself into as tight a ball as his girth would allow, he closed his eyes and Harriet chuckled. He mightn't be able to speak but, oh boy, could he let her know how he was feeling!

Still seeing him curled up like that, a grey bundle of injured pride and hurt feelings, had awakened the germ of an idea inside her. She snatched up the sketchpad from the pine dresser and sat down at the table, anxious to translate all that offended dignity to paper. Quickly her pencil raced over the blank white sheets, making a dozen or so lightning sketches, until she was satisfied that she had every line perfect. Then and only then was it time to put the sketches into the context she intended; another episode of *King Caspar the Cat*, a cartoon serial run by one of the top daily papers which was fast establishing Harriet as one of the top cartoonists in the country.

Lifting the heavy drawing-board up from its usual hidey-hole behind the kitchen door, she set it on to the scrubbed pine table and clipped a fresh sheet of paper into place. She had exchanged the thin point of a pencil for a bold black ink pen, and soon several sheets were filled with its thick strokes as she drew and wrote in the captions.

Several hours later Harriet sat back, easing her pen-stiffened fingers while she ran her eyes critically over the work. She felt a quiet glow of satisfaction fill her as she realised just how good the cartoons were. She was a perfectionist, preferring to destroy hours of work rather than turn in something she didn't consider up to her standards, but today she'd been lucky. Today everything had turned out perfectly, and from the look of it there was enough material to complete a whole week's episodes of the strip. If she kept this work-rate up for the next few days then at least she wouldn't have to worry about getting nothing done while she was away this coming week.

She crossed the room and poured herself a cup of the now-stale coffee, sipping at it while she let her mind spin forwards in time to the coming days, and it was all she could do to bite back a groan. Why on earth had she done it? What in the name of heaven had possessed her to volunteer her services...she must have been mad! Quickly her thoughts raced over a few million possible excuses to get her out of the commitment, but deep down she knew there was no way she could use even one of them. She'd promised Jill that she would go and fill in for her, and it was on the basis of this promise that her sister had agreed to accept the holiday. There was just no way she could go back on her word now, no way at all.

Like it or not, come Saturday she was going camping for one whole week...along with fifteen cub scouts. Lord help her! Mind you, one thing was certain, it couldn't be any worse than what she'd just faced that morning!

The roadway was a moving, waving sea of dark green, and Harriet had to blink her eyes rapidly till she could distinguish one small form from the other. Jill had told her that there were fifteen boys booked to go on the camp, but to her inexperienced eyes it looked a lot more than that. Every inch of the pavement was crammed with boys clad in the regulation grey shorts, green sweaters and bright neckties, and she sent up a silent prayer that her eyes were playing tricks; fifteen she could probably cope with, but this bunch—well, that was something else! But still, it was too late to be having second thoughts now, and taking a deep breath she opened the car door and went to join them, weaving her way through the crowd till she reached the capable-looking woman standing next to a rather battered minibus.

'Pat.'

Hearing her name, the woman spun round, a smile brightening her pleasant, homely face as she saw who was calling her.

'Harriet! Oh, am I glad to see you. For a few minutes I thought you weren't going to make it either, like this lot.'

Holding out a sheet of foolscap paper, she ran a finger down the column of names, tapping it sharply against each one of the crosses. 'All these have backed out!'

'What do you mean, "backed out"?'

Taking the list from her, Harriet ran her eyes down the neatly printed names, her stomach sinking under a sudden wave of apprehension. 'Surely you don't mean all these men have now decided not to come and help out, do you?'

'I do. There were eight "dads" booked to come on the camp when we first planned the trip, but now we're down to just one, plus you, me and my husband, Ted, of course.'

'But surely they can't do that?'

There was a note of desperation to Harriet's usually soft tones. Pushing the soft, curly strands of deep auburn hair from her cheeks, she studied the list more closely, hoping against hope that Pat had made some sort of mistake, but of course, she hadn't. Every one of the 'dads' except Danny's friend Mike's had cancelled . . . the rats!

'They can and they have,' Pat answered simply, 'and it's not the first time it's happened, either.'

'It's not?'

'Oh, no. I can't even count the number of times we've organised trips only to have more than half the parents back out at the very last moment. Still we'll manage, we'll have to. We can't disappoint the boys now, can we?' she asked with a slight smile, and Harriet nodded, wishing she could summon up even a smidgen of the older woman's confidence. In truth, the ratio of four adults to fifteen children seemed reasonable, so maybe she was just being silly to feel so dismayed. Anyway, as Pat had so rightly said, there was no way they could cancel the holiday and disappoint the boys, so she'd best make the most of it and knuckle down to some work.

'What do you want me to do, anyway, Pat, now I'm here?' she asked quickly before her resolve disappeared. 'Shall I start packing these into the bus?'

Pat looked down at the heaped pile of kit-bags and luggage, and shook her head.

'No, they're to go in the trailer once Ted has finished loading the cooking pots and utensils. Really, I don't think there's much you can do just at the moment, everything is more or less under control, if that's the right word to describe this chaos. We'll load up all the gear first, then we can get the boys settled in the bus later, I think.'

'Are they all coming with us? There seem to be far more than I expected.' Harriet gazed round at the roadful of green-capped figures, a small frown puckering the smooth, pale skin of her forehead as she realised her first impression had been dreadfully accurate.

'Lord, no. We've got fifteen booked to come with us, though typically they've not all arrived yet. The rest have just come along to see them off.'

'Well, thank heavens for that,' Harriet murmured fervently, and Pat laughed in sympathy, knowing how overwhelming it must all seem to a novice.

A couple of boys came up to claim Pat's attention, and Harriet moved aside. Pulling the soft lemon sweatshirt down over her slim jean-clad hips, she looked round for Danny, but after several minutes concentrated study of the crowd of boys realised her nephew was nowhere in sight and bit back a small sigh of annoyance. She'd hoped to have a few minutes with him before they set off, to check he had everything he needed, but now it looked as if she'd not get the chance, and just for a moment wished she'd insisted he stay at her house this past week. Oh, deep down she knew Jill had been right when she'd said he would enjoy staying with his friend far more, and that Harriet needed some free time to get ahead on her work, but at least it would have saved all this last-minute hassle...not to mention all the agonising she'd gone through last night!

Walking further away from the chattering boys, she stared across the road, her eyes sweeping down over the green fields to the woods which surrounded Abbey Lakes, while her mind ran back over the half-hour she'd wasted dithering in front of the phone the night before. Three times she'd picked up the receiver, and three times she'd slammed it back down without dialling the number, and why? Because there'd been no way she'd wanted to make the call and end up having to speak to that American again, that was why. No, once had been quite enough to last her a lifetime, thank you! Still, duty had dictated that she make the call, and she had…eventually. Though it sounded foolish to admit it now, she'd been more than a little relieved when no one had answered. The antipathy she felt for that man was still so strong that even now, nearly a week since that dreadful morning, it could fill her with a deep, burning anger: to think he'd insulted her, manhandled her and that she'd been virtually powerless to stop him! It was unbelievable, or would be if the memory of it wasn't so vividly clear. No, the less chance she had of coming into contact with him again, the better!

'Harry! Hey, Harry!'

The familiar childish voice calling her name brought her thoughts abruptly back to the present, and she looked along the road to see Danny working his way through the pack, closely followed by a blond-haired boy who just had to be his friend Mike. Within seconds they were at her side and she smiled down at them both.

'Well, I was beginning to think you'd changed your minds and weren't coming.'

'Yes, I know we're late but Mike had to go and see his Dad in the hospital first before we left.'

'Hospital? Why, what on earth's happened?' she demanded, turning her attention to the boy standing quietly at Danny's side.

'He had an accident at work yesterday; some barrels dropped off a truck and hit him. He's got a broken arm and a couple of cracked ribs, but Mom says he'll be OK in a few weeks.'

More than a trace of worry laced the boy's voice, and impulsively Harriet leaned down and hugged him.

'I'm sure he'll be just fine, Mike. You'll see, in a couple of weeks he'll be as good as new, so don't worry.'

Then suddenly the full meaning of his words hit her, and she straightened up in dismay.

'But of course that means he won't be coming on camp with us, doesn't it?'

'I'm afraid not, he's still in the hospital, but it doesn't really matter 'cause Rick's said he'll come instead and help out. Look, there he is now.'

Mike pointed to a spot past her shoulder, and slowly Harriet turned, eyes locking on the tall figure making his way through the boys towards them. She felt her breath catch in her throat in sheer horror. Surely it couldn't be, surely the fates couldn't be so cruel...could they?

Closing her eyes, she murmured a fervent little prayer that it was all just a rather nasty hallucination sprung from the memories which had been haunting her all week.

'So, it seems we're destined to meet again, after all, Miss Prince.'

There was no mistaking that soft American accent with its underlying hint of steel and, opening her eyes, Harriet stared dumbly up at him, once again unable to think of one single thing to say!

Ten minutes later the shock-waves of horror rolling through her body had subsided just enough to enable her to think and, with luck, find a solution to the dilemma, not that it was going to be that easy. As far as she could see there were just two choices; either he stayed and she left, or she stayed and he left...the camp just wasn't going to be big enough for both of them. The question was just how could she expect Pat to understand her feelings without telling her all the details of what had gone on between them?

Colour washed under the fine pale skin of her face and neck in an angry tide, and hastily she turned away and busied herself sorting the bags to be stacked in the trailer. There was just no way she wanted to go into the details of what had happened that morning, no way she wanted to explain how he'd manhandled her, nor what he'd said to her over the telephone later. The embarrassment was still too fresh and vivid to allow her to share it with anyone, even Pat, whom she'd known for years. No, she had to find a way of convincing Pat that perhaps it wouldn't be a good idea to allow Rick Dawson to come with them to camp, and that, from the look of things, could be a monumental task.

Since he'd arrived, the man had gone out of his way to make a good impression, and from the look on Pat's face now he had obviously succeeded. He'd turned on the charm and poor Pat had fallen for it hook, line and giant sinker. Now Harriet had the deep-seated feeling that she'd be hard pushed to convince Pat that the hundred and sixty pounds of green-eyed charisma standing nonchalantly next to her could do any wrong. She picked up one of the kit-bags and tossed it to Ted with rather more force than was necessary!

Catching the bag which had hit him hard in the stomach, Ted shot her a swift look, fast noting the angry colour which stained her usually pale skin, and a trace of concern edged his voice as he asked softly, 'Are you all right, Harry? You look a bit flushed.' And Harriet felt a quick twinge of shame stab at her for giving vent to her ill temper.

'Oh, I'm fine, thanks Ted—just a bit of a headache starting, that's all,' she muttered quickly, saying the first thing that sprang to mind which could explain her behaviour.

'Mmm, well, I hope you're not coming down with that virus that's been knocking around; that starts with a headache,' Ted said glumly, still watching her with concern.

'Does it?'

An idea was forming rapidly in her mind at his words, an idea which could prove to be the solution to all her present problems. What if she claimed to be feeling ill, as Ted had suggested, too ill to make it possible for her to travel? It would mean she could go home, lock her door and forget about that wretched man... for ever!

'What do you two think, then? She looks a bit flushed to me.' Ted spoke to someone behind her and Harriet spun round, eyes darkening with scarcely veiled temper as she met the green ones which were studying her so intently. She'd been so engrossed in her thoughts that she'd not heard him come up, and now he was standing so close she felt herself go rigid as the heat from his body warmed her skin. Quickly she took a couple of steps back and looked away, striving for some measure of calm, some coolant for the hot temper which was threatening to boil over.

'Actually you do look a bit flushed, Harriet,' Pat said, studying her closely. 'What do you think, Rick?'

There was no way Harriet wanted to hear his opinion on how she looked, no way at all, and she spoke hurriedly before he could answer.

'I'm fine, Pat, don't worry. It's just a bit of a headache, that's all.'

'Are you sure now, Harriet—certain that you feel up to coming with us?' Pat insisted. 'Perhaps it would be better if you went home and see how you feel later.'

It was the opening she'd wanted, the chance to escape from the prospect of seven days in Rick Dawson's company, and Harriet was about to take it when out of the corner of her eye she caught the tiniest glimpse of the expression on his face and stopped abruptly. He knew, damn him, knew she was lying, knew that his unexpected arrival had upset her, knew he was the real reason for her sudden illness, and he was standing there, laughing at her! But she'd show him, all right, she'd show him. There was no way that 'thug' was going to stand there and mock her.

Pushing the clinging curls from her cheeks, she stood up a touch straighter and smiled warmly back at Pat who was still waiting for her answer.

'I'll be fine, Pat, really—well enough to travel. There's no way I want to go back home now.'

'Not even to get rid of that headache?' a soft voice enquired gently, and Harriet wondered if it was only she who could hear the mockery in its tone. She gazed up into his face for a brief moment, her lips curved into a polite and friendly smile while her brown eyes shot him a quite different message.

'Why, no, Mr Dawson, there's just no way I want to miss this trip for anything, not even a week-long headache!'

She walked sedately round the trailer, followed by a low chuckle of appreciative male laughter. If he thought he was going to have it all his own way this week, take every opportunity to disconcert her, then he could think again. He might have scored on points when they'd gone their first round that other morning, but from now on she was looking for a straight knock-out . . . with her as the victor!

'Do I detect just the tiniest hint of friction between you and that gorgeous man?'

Pat had followed her round the trailer and was eyeing her closely, and swiftly Harriet bent down and began packing wellington boots into a canvas sack with scant regard for any kind of order.

'I don't know what you mean, Pat.'

'Don't you? Well, I suppose that's your story and you're going to stick to it, but I can tell you one thing, love.'

'What?' Pausing in her hasty untidy packing, Harriet looked up warily, wondering just what she would say.

'That this promises to be the most interesting camp I've ever been on...and I can hardly wait to get started!'

With a last smile she walked away, leaving Harriet still crouched over the pile of tangled wellies. Slowly her eyes slid back to the tall figure propped against the side of the trailer, and a chill little shiver of unease raced its way icily down her spine. She had the sudden nasty feeling that this week could prove to be more interesting than Pat could even begin to imagine!

CHAPTER THREE

'OH, PAT, no, surely there's another way?'

'I'm sorry, Harry, but there isn't, really. I'll have to go in the bus with Ted to keep an eye on the boys, and Rick Dawson will have to go with you.'

'But why can't I take some of the boys in the car and let him go in the bus?' Desperately Harriet searched round for another answer, anything which would mean she didn't have to spend near three hours closeted in the car with that man for company.

'I'm sorry, Harriet, but it's a question of insurance, you see, as much as anything. The boys are insured as a group, but only if they're using our official transport. There's no way I can get round it; he either goes with you or walks.'

It was a tempting choice, and Harriet knew with absolute certainty which one she would make if it was left to her. She'd had Rick Dawson in a car with her once and look just where it had got her... pushed up against the bonnet while he frisked her! She needed another go at that like she needed a hole in her head, but looking at Pat's face she knew there was no way she could sway her. Rules were rules, and as far as Pat was concerned there was little reason to break them.

'Right, then, we'd best get started if we want to get the camp set up before tea time, hadn't we? Rick,' Pat called over to where he was standing deep in conversation with Ted, 'will you go with Harriet? I'm afraid there's not enough room in the bus for you, and anyway she'll probably be glad of some company on the way. It's a good three-hour drive till we get there.'

'Sure, Pat, that's fine with me.' He walked over and nodded towards the bus before continuing, 'Those wooden bench seats look kinda hard to me anyway, so I think I'll prefer a bit of luxury in Harriet's car.'

There was a moment's brief, puzzled silence, then Ted laughed. 'Comfort, in Betsy? Guess you don't know what Harriet's car is like, do you, Rick?'

'Sure I do. After all, she drove me back from the airport in it the day I arrived,' he answered, looking puzzled, and Harriet had to turn quickly away to hide her laughter as she realised his mistake. He obviously still believed that the taxi was hers and that they would be going away to camp in it, but was he in for a shock, and was it a big one! Fond as she was of Betsy, by no stretch of the imagination could she class her as comfortable! Still, it would serve him right, pay him back just a tiny fraction for the dreadful way he had treated her that day. In fact, it was almost worth having to put up with his company for the next few hours just to see his face when he finally realised his error and met Betsy!

It was a lovely thought, a wonderful prospect, and, pulling the keys from her pocket, Harriet turned towards him, a smile of saccharine sweetness curving her lips.

'Well then, Mr Dawson, as long as you're quite happy with the arrangements, we may as well be on our way.'

It was difficult to keep the laughter from her voice, but Harriet really thought she'd managed it till she caught the expression in the green eyes which were studying her closely, and realised she might have been just a trifle careless. Rick Dawson may have acted like a rough tough thug when they'd first met, but he was far from stupid; he'd seen the smile, heard the tone and was now trying to work out just what had caused them!

'Oh, Harry, before you go, let me run over the directions to the campsite with you.'

Pat's voice broke the small silence which had fallen over the group, and thankfully Harriet turned towards her, feigning an interest in what she was saying while in truth her attention was still locked in a quite different direction. Would he work it out? Would he realise that her sudden acceptance of his company stemmed from some emotion other than kindness? She hoped not. Rick Dawson deserved something for the other morning, and Harriet was determined he was going to get it!

'Right, that's it, then, Harry. If you use the map and just be wary at that crossroads as I've explained, then you shouldn't have any trouble. Here you are.'

Briskly Pat pushed a folded square of paper into Harriet's hand, and she started, realising with a sinking heart that she'd not heard one word the other woman had told her. Quickly she looked down, eyes tracing desperately over the map, and was relieved to find that the route had been clearly marked in red; surely with that to follow she'd have no problem, would she?

'Well, then, I think that's it. We might as well get off and see you both later. Take care.'

With a smile Pat headed towards the bus, and as Ted pulled out, she leant from the window to wave to the rest of the pack, who were giving them a rousing send-off. Within minutes the bus had disappeared, the rest of the boys were on their way and Harriet suddenly realised there were just two people left in the quiet roadway...her and Rick Dawson. She stole a quick look in his direction, colour flaring under her skin as she saw she was still the centre of his attention. Looking down, she made a great show of folding the map Pat had given her into a square small enough to fit into the back pocket of her jeans, cursing softly as the car keys slid from her fumbling fingers. She went to scoop them up, but froze as her hand brushed against the hard, lean masculine one which had beaten her to it.

'Allow me.'

The deep voice rumbled close to her ear, and quickly Harriet straightened, stepping back a pace to allow some distance between them. Her breath seemed to be air-locked in her chest, as though her lungs had stopped inflating, and desperately she fought to relax, chiding herself for being so nervous. True, she intended to trick him, give him a little discomfort, but just what could he do if and when he realised it? Nothing, absolutely and totally nothing!

The thought gave her fresh heart, boosted up her sagging courage, and holding out her hand she let him drop the keys into it before saying calmly, 'Thank you. Now, I think we'd better be off, don't you?'

She headed back along the road to where she'd left Betsy neatly parked at the end of a row of gleaming motors.

'I wonder why I get the strangest feeling that you're planning something, Miss Prince.'

He'd come up close alongside her, soft-footed in the old scuffed trainers he wore, and Harriet quickly eased herself over on the narrow pavement, away from the disturbing feel of his arm brushing against her shoulder. Although he was leanly built, there was a hardness to his body which hinted at the strength she'd already had a taste of, and it took an enormous effort to quell the nervous shudder which suddenly threatened her body. There were barely a half dozen cars between them and

Betsy now, a mere handful of paces before she could spring her little surprise, and there was no way she was going to let anything spoil it!

Looking sideways, she summoned up one of her coolest little smiles and said calmly, 'I'm sorry, Mr Dawson, I don't think I know what you mean.'

'Don't you? Well, I suppose we'll soon see, but, lady, I just know you're up to something. I can sense it.'

Not even the tiniest hint of worry filtered through the mockery in his green eyes, and hastily Harriet looked away as she felt her temper once more begin to flare. He was so goddamned sure of himself, so certain, that it made her itch to give him something which would really disconcert him. If ever a man deserved what was coming, it was Mr Infuriating Rick Dawson!

Temper quickened her pace so that within seconds they were at the end of the row of cars, and she watched as he looked round, a small frown creasing the tanned skin of his forehead. He hadn't bothered to shave that morning, and stubble darkened his firm-cut jaw, adding even more to the overall impression of toughness, but now, about to play her ace, Harriet was quite unperturbed and stood quietly waiting for him to deal the question.

'Where's the car?'

Dropping his gaze, Rick finally centred his attention on Harriet, and she smiled sweetly back at him for one glorious moment which oozed with anticipation.

'Here.'

Delicately she eased the key into the lock, jiggling it round with a skill which told of long years of practice, till finally it connected, and swinging the door open she stepped aside.

'Do get in, Mr Dawson, or we're going to be awfully late in arriving.'

'Now, hold it, lady.'

A large hand clamped itself round the slender knob of her shoulder, and Harriet stopped dead, her face freezing over.

'Please take your hand off me...I still have the bruises from the other morning when you grabbed me, and I don't need another set, thank you!'

Icy sarcasm dripped from her voice, and she saw him flinch before he dropped his hand from her shoulder and stepped back a pace, folding his arms across his chest as though to resist any further temptations. His eyes slid slowly over the small car, then on to Harriet, studying her set expression for a few silent moments before he spoke.

'If I promise not to lay another finger on you, do you think you could tell me just what's going on?'

His voice was low and soft against the morning's stillness, and Harriet felt her breath start to flow a little easier. His sudden, unexpected grab at her shoulder had startled her, reminding her so vividly of their last unpleasant encounter, but she couldn't afford to let it throw her. This might be her one and only chance to pay him back...and there was no way she was going to miss it!

'Going on? I'm sorry, but I don't know what you mean,' she said quietly, a hint of feigned puzzlement to her voice.

'Oh, come on, don't take that line with me, honey, you know exactly what I'm on about. We're supposed to be going off to camp in your car, so just why are you asking me to get into this...this heap of junk? My God, it doesn't even look as though it will move, let alone take us on a three-hour journey. There's just no way we can travel in it . . . no way at all!'

That stung. Old and rather battered Betsy might be, but she was far from junk, and Harriet took an instant exception to his words. She ran a gentle, protective hand over the deep yellow paintwork, idly noting the odd patches of blue marbling the surface where the previous colour was showing through.

'Well?'

Arms still folded across his chest, he stared down at her with obvious impatience, and Harriet felt a tiny ripple of malicious glee curl through her as she studied his face. Evidently the prospect of travelling in the car was far from his idea of pleasure, and that suited her fine. Her first plan when she'd realised she was stuck with his company had been to give him a little discomfort, but maybe she could achieve more that that: maybe if he found the idea of travelling in Betsy so unappealing, then he'd decide not to go, and that would be absolutely and totally perfect. The thought gave her fresh heart, gave her the strength to bite back a more snappy answer, and, pinning a faint smile to her lips, she said calmly,

'This heap of junk, as you call it, happens to be my car, Mr Dawson, the one I intend going away to camp in.'

'Your car . . . but what happened to the other one, the taxi you were driving the other morning?'

Puzzlement creased his brow into tanned furrows, and Harriet paused for a second, determined to wring the last drop of pleasure from the moment, then answered slowly and very, very clearly, 'I'm afraid that wasn't mine; I'd just borrowed it to get to the airport, you see. This is the car I'll be using, but of course it's up to you if you want to join me. It's your choice entirely.'

She walked round the car and, opening the door, slid inside, trying hard not to give way to laughter. His face had been a study when she'd told him, a mixture of shock, dismay and utter horror, and for a moment a feeling of triumph raced hotly through her. There was no way he'd consider coming now, no way he'd risk travelling in poor, battered Betsy. She'd done it, played her hand and won the game. Whistling softly she slid the key into the ignition and started the engine, smiling as the car responded with a well-heeled purr before settling down into a nice, steady rhythm, an omen for the coming journey.

There was a sudden flurry of movement at her side, and Harriet swung round, startled, eyes widening with shock as they met the green ones now on her level.

'Right, as you were saying, we'd better be off, then, hadn't we, if we don't want to be late?'

Rick settled back in the seat and fastened the seat-belt, raising a thick, quizzical eyebrow in her direction when she failed to respond but just sat there, gaping.

'Well?'

Mockery laced the deep voice, mockery and more than a hint of challenge, and with a snarl Harriet slammed the small car into gear and pulled out into the roadway. She might have played her cards right, but it seemed he was the one who'd just won the game!

The next few miles passed in a complete and total silence, and Harriet thanked heaven for the fact that traffic was light on the narrow country roads. Her mind was in a turmoil, making it difficult to concentrate on anything other than the whole host of unpleasant thoughts which writhed snakelike inside her, most of them centred on the man sitting quietly next to her. Given his scathing comments just minutes earlier, she'd been sure he'd not come, so sure, in fact, that his sudden appearance in the next seat had completely thrown her. Now she had to face not only the next three hours in his company, but the next seven days as well; the question was, how would she ever stand it?

Ever since they'd first met, when she'd come back and found him in Ken's taxi, he'd rubbed her up the wrong way. He was trouble in great big foot-high letters, and there was no way she could see that ever changing. Why, if she added up the actual time they'd spent together, it must barely make an hour, yet most of that had been spent in fighting. So how on earth could she be expected to pass a whole week in his company without World War Three erupting? It was hopeless, absolutely hopeless, and she just had to make him see it. She pulled in to a lay-by and cut the engine, taking a deep breath before she turned to him and said quietly, 'We have to talk.'

Rick unclipped the seat-belt and eased his legs round in the cramped space till he could face her, green eyes running over the soft curves of her face with an unreadable expression in them which flicked at her taut nerve-ends like a whip.

'What about?'

His voice was low, easy, unruffled, and just for a moment Harriet felt annoyance run through her. Did nothing worry him . . . ever? It seemed not, but still, this was neither the time nor the place to pursue it. Now she had to concentrate on keeping everything as calm and sensible as possible, somehow convince him that what she proposed was the only solution; and she hastily bit back her irritation.

'About us, of course.'

'Us? Mmm, that sounds interesting. What is it about "us" you wish to discuss, then, Miss . . . Harriet?'

His tone put a whole new emphasis on her words, and Harriet felt her cheeks flame with unwelcome colour as she heard it. He was deliberately misunderstanding her, baiting her, but there was no way she was going to let it deter her, and faced him squarely, a steely light to her brown eyes.

'You know exactly what I mean, *Mr Dawson*, and it's not "us" in that connotation, either!'

'Pity,' he murmured softly, sliding his arm along the back of her seat. Harriet caught her breath in a soft gasp as she felt his fingers brush gently against the warm nape of her neck under the curling tendrils of auburn hair. She pushed at his fingers, but only succeeded in dislodging them so that they dropped on to the curve of her shoulder.

'Will you stop that?' she demanded hotly.

'Stop what? This?' Slowly he traced a pattern over the soft curve of flesh, a gentle caress which set her nerve-ends tingling. She jerked forwards, sliding to the very edge of her seat to escape his touch. Her breath was tight in her chest, her blood racing, though whether from pleasure or sheer temper it was hard to decide, and she wasted no time in trying. The situation was fast getting out of hand, running in an entirely different direction from what she had intended, and she said harshly, 'Look, I don't know what you think you're playing at, but please stop it.'

Her face was stormy, her eyes burning, and for an instant he hesitated, his eyes studying her closely before, reaching out, he caught her hand in his and said softly, 'I'm sorry, I was only teasing. What did you want to talk to me about?'

His hand was warm, firm, the skin slightly rough against the softness of hers, evoking a sudden wave of sensation, and hastily Harriet pulled her fingers free, not wanting to be swayed from her decision. Rick Dawson could be charming, all right, but as far as she was concerned it was all on the surface and there was no way she was going to be fool enough to soften. Fixing him with a level stare, she fought hard to ignore the faint tremor which still rippled through her, tiny wavelets of lingering sensation.

'Look, Mr Dawson, let's cut out all the play-acting, shall we, and lay it on the line? There's just no way you and I can spend a week together on this camp, no way at all.'

'Why?'

'*Why?* What do you mean, "why"?' she demanded. 'It's obvious, isn't it? You and I just don't jell, that's the whole top and bottom of it, and there's just nothing we can do to change it.'

'No? I mean, no—it seems like that. So just what do you suggest we do?' he asked steadily, eyes tracing over her stormy face.

'It's obvious, surely: one of us has to back out, and frankly I think it should be you.'

'No way,' he said firmly, a hard set to his chiselled lips.

'Why not?'

'Because I promised Mike I'd go when his father was hurt, and there's no way I intend to break that promise, that's why. If you can't handle being on camp with me, then that's your problem, and it's up to you to pull out. I'm going and that's absolutely final.'

'But I can't back out, I promised my sister I'd go,' she wailed.

'Well, then, it looks as if you'll just have to put up with it, won't you? Still, you never know, you might find it's not so bad as you imagined. You might even find that you come to like me.'.

'*Like* you? You must be joking. Why, I've as much chance of making friends with a rattlesnake as I have with you. There's no way I'm going to end up liking you.'

'No? Well, we'll see, I suppose, but somehow I've got the strangest feeling you might change your mind.'

'Never!' she said hotly, starting up the engine with a mighty roar.

He ran a gentle finger down the flushed warmth of her cheek, his green eyes sparkling with mischief and a gentle mocking laughter.

'Never is a long time, honey—a very long time, so how can you be so certain?'

'I am certain, absolutely and totally certain. I wouldn't like you if you were the last man on earth.'

'Well, as I said, we'll soon see,' he said easily, settling back in his seat. 'But do you know, there's just one thing I can't resist?'

'What's that?' she snapped, pulling back on to the roadway. 'Terrorising women?'

He chuckled softly, his green eyes gleaming in swift appreciation of the barb. 'A challenge, Harriet, honey, that's what. And it seems to me you've just thrown down the gauntlet.'

Open-mouthed, she shot him a swift glance, her heart stumbling as she caught sight of the determination on his tanned face.

'What do you mean?'

'I mean that before the end of this week you're going to change your mind about me; you're going to find you like me more than you could ever have imagined.'

'Never,' she snapped. 'Never, never, *never*!' And wondered why her voice sounded suddenly frightened.

Checking her mirror, Harriet eased the car over to the slip road, glad to be leaving the motorway at last. She hated driving on motorways with an intense and burning passion, and had only done so today in the knowledge that it would speed up the journey and that glorious moment when she could get Rick Dawson out of the car. Skimming a look sideways in his direction, she was glad to see that he was still sleeping as he had been for the past hour. At least she'd been spared the effort of making conversation with him, something she knew would have been impossible just at the moment. His words were still hammering round and round in her head, making her pulse beat with the rhythm of them, and though she knew it was foolish and silly to let them upset her, somehow they did. There was no way she could ever see him succeeding in the so-called challenge, no way at all, so why did his threat seem so strangely ominous? It puzzled her.

'Tired?'

The low-voiced question startled her, and she felt the car swerve a fraction as she jerked at the wheel. Steadying it, she slowed down and negotiated the huge roundabout which marked the end of the motorway system before she answered, 'A little. I always find motorway driving a strain.' Her tone was as coolly neutral as she could manage, betraying little of her inward agitation.

'You should have let me take a turn, then. Why on earth didn't you ask me?'

Easing up on the seat, Rick stretched the cramped muscles in his back and shoulders, his arm brushing softly against hers, and she had to fight back an instant desire to flinch away from the brief contact. There was no way she wanted him to realise just how nervous she felt around him now, no way she wanted him to know she was anything but immune to his presence. She had the deep-seated feeling he would only use the knowledge to his advantage.

'I didn't really think you'd jump at the chance to drive, having heard what you thought of the car earlier,' she said coldly.

'Mmm, well, maybe I was a little harsh back there, but can you blame me? There was I, expecting a nice comfortable journey in that other car, and you threw this at me.'

'You didn't have to come, did you? I gave you the offer of staying back . . . twice, if I remember correctly,' she said with a total lack of compassion.

'So I noticed.'

There was a wry note to his voice, and Harriet shot him a swift glance, wondering just what had caused it.

'I'm not used to having my company rejected with so much...enthusiasm, if you want to know, honey. I can't say it does a lot for my ego,' he explained with a low, self-mocking laugh.

'I'm sure you'll survive,' she replied frostily turning her attention back to her driving.

'Oh, I'm sure I shall; probably even be a better person for the experience.'

'Well, you couldn't be worse, that's for sure,' she snapped tartly, and he laughed.

'You sure know how to flatter a guy, don't you? But still, it only makes me even more determined to change your mind.'

And instantly Harriet rued her snappy answer. She'd get nowhere with him if she didn't try and stay cool, absolutely nowhere, and she had to remember it. The trouble was, every time she opened her mouth another side of her took over, a side which blew all caution to the wind and just wanted to give him as good as she got, plus ten per cent extra! It was a habit she must try to break...and soon.

Still, his words had given her some insight into just why he'd seen her hostility as such a challenge. He was obviously more used to receiving adulation from the female population, so her blatant refusal to succumb to his charms really grated. She quickly ran assessing eyes over him from head to toe, and had to admit it was little wonder he usually set female hearts pounding with desire rather than anger. Even dressed in worn jeans and an old navy sweater, he looked good, his lean body hard and well muscled, his thick blond hair and tanned skin appealingly healthy. Although he was by no means conventionally handsome, the firm cut of his features and that hint of toughness was attractive...if you liked that sort of combination. Not that Harriet did, of course; her preference usually ran to something a little less aggressively masculine than Rick Dawson's charms, but still, she could see how he would appeal to a lot of other women; the pity of it was, they wouldn't be on camp to distract him. Perhaps, though, that was the clue to surviving this coming week; perhaps if she stopped bruising his ego with her punches and tried to soothe it with a little softness then he'd lose interest and give up this silly challenge. Surely it was worth a try...if she could stand it!

'Well, what have you decided? Do I pass or not?'

Abruptly drawn from her reverie by the sudden question, Harriet shot him a swift look, flushing as she caught the mocking expression on his tanned face. He'd obviously seen the look and guessed just where her thoughts were wandering. The trouble was, he seemed to have drawn entirely the wrong conclusion and, casting all thoughts of softness aside, she answered swiftly, 'You don't even make the grade as far as I'm concerned, Mr Dawson, so there's no way you'll ever pass in my estimation.'

'Really? Do you know I'd be real cut up about that if I thought you meant it, Harriet? Real cut up, especially when I'm starting to have such warm feelings about you.'

He was baiting her, Harriet knew it, but couldn't stop herself from responding. 'You can keep your warm feelings, Rick Dawson, and you know just what...'

'Now, now! Is that a ladylike way to respond to a compliment, honey? I'm shocked... and I thought you British girls were all so very prim and proper!'

And Harriet bit back a few thousand spiky answers. She had to remember her resolve to handle the situation with composure, but something told her it wasn't going to be easy. Rick Dawson had an unerring ability to ignite more sparks in her than any other man had ever managed! But still, she had to try; firming her lips into a polite smile, she decided it was time to change the subject to something a little less inflammatory.

'We seem to be making good time, don't we?'

'On the journey, you mean?' he asked with a slight grin, and Harriet prayed to heaven for a bit of patience. Refusing to summon up an answer to such a blatant piece of innuendo, she merely nodded, sighing with relief when he didn't push it.

'Yes, we do. I've got to admit I may owe you an apology for what I said earlier; this old car keeps up a fair speed when she's going. How long have you had her?'

'Oh, about four years now. I bought her just after I'd left art college, and somehow I've never had the heart to change her,' she answered, relieved they'd at last found a fairly safe topic.

'Art college? Is that what you do, then? Are you an artist, not a taxi driver as I previously imagined?' he asked with a slow grin, and Harriet chuckled softly, finding it easier to handle this sort of interest.

'No, I'm not a taxi driver, as you so rightly guessed, though I suppose I'm not an artist in the sense you mean it, either. I'm a cartoonist.'

'A cartoonist?'

She had his interest now, she could sense it, and was glad. If she could just keep him to a few safer topics for the rest of journey, then maybe they wouldn't come to blows, after all. Shooting a glance at the small digital clock she'd stuck to the wooden dashboard, she did a few quick calculations and realised that if Pat's reckoning was correct there was bárely an hour's travelling time left till they reached the campsite. Surely two supposedly sane and adult people could pass that in some sort of harmony...couldn't they? The thought gave her hope, inspired her to answer the query in his voice in rather more detail than she would have previously.

'Mmm, yes. I took a course in graphic design at college, intending to go into book illustration. I'd always been interested in drawing cartoons, though, always enjoyed the challenge of getting both humour and a message into a few brief pictures, but had never really thought I could earn a living at it.'

'So what made you change your mind?'

Swivelling sideways in his seat, Rick gave her his full attention, and quickly Harriet forced down the small uprush of pleasure at his obviously genuine interest. She had to remember what he'd said earlier, and not let a bit of flattery go to her usually more-than-level head.

'It was one of my tutors at college, really. He convinced me that I could make a go of it if I was really serious and set my mind to it. I worked up a portfolio of cartoons I'd done over the years, plus an idea I had for a strip serial, and sent it to several of the top circulation papers, but with no success. Then Tom, my tutor, suggested I aimed a bit lower, tried to make a name in the provincial papers first before trying for the nationals. I took his advice and found it worked. The serial ran in one of the local Lancashire papers for just over a year before I started getting enquiries from further afield. Now, it's run by one of the nationals, you may even have seen it since you've been here. It's called *King Caspar the Cat.*'

'I have, indeed. In fact, I've made a point of reading it these past few days as it always makes me laugh. Where on earth do you get your ideas from?'

Harriet chuckled, a soft, low sound which was unconsciously attractive.

'From the original, of course; Caspar is my cat and most of it's based on his adventures... with a little literary licence, of course.'

'Well, from what I've seen, you must have your time cut out if even part of it is true,' Rick said with a laugh. 'But it's funny, you know, somehow I'd gained the impression it was drawn by a man; I can't remember the name on it, but I'd bet several dollars it's not a woman's.'

There was a puzzled note to his voice which Harriet could well appreciate. Her choice of name for her work had been a conscious decision, based on the fact that most cartoonists, or at least the top ones, were men. She had been determined that she was going to be among this group, and that nothing, especially nothing as un-important as a name, would hold her back.

'I go under the name Harry Prince when I work,' she said briefly, 'so it is my name but can be interpreted any way you please.'

'Until people meet you...then they're in absolutely no doubt,' he said softly, and Harriet flushed with a sudden wave of remembered annoyance.

'That's good, coming from you,' she answered sharply.

'What do you mean?'

'I mean that you were the one who thought I was a boy when we first met, weren't you?'

'Yes, and heaven alone knows how it was possible, even given that strange outfit you were wearing. I must have been even more tired than I imagined.'

There was a soft, almost seductive note to his deep voice, and instantly Harriet regretted having brought up the subject. They'd done so well for these past few minutes, keeping everything on such a level and stable footing, that there was no way she wanted to set it all back rocking. She had the uneasy feeling she couldn't handle that sort of motion!

Still, she had to face the fact that their previous meeting was now an indelible part of history, and that no amount of wishing could change it. She'd get no-where trying to pretend it never happened, and nowhere at all by losing her temper. Checking her mirror, she pulled out and overtook a slow-moving pair of cyclists, waiting till she'd completed the manoeuvre before she spoke.

'Did you find your wallet, by the way?' Her tone was carefully cool and level, and she felt immensely proud of herself for the effort.

'No, I'm afraid not. I guess I must have dropped it somewhere, probably coming through Customs.'

'What a shame! It must be an awful blow when you've just started your holiday,' she answered swiftly, a hint of genuine sympathy to her tone.

'Yes, it is a nuisance. Not exactly the best start I've ever had to a holiday, one way and another,' he answered quietly. There was a dryness to his voice, but Harriet ignored it, not wanting to rake over old coals and start yet another fire burning.

She centred her attention on the winding road they were following and said casually, 'What do you do for a living? We seem to have talked all about me so far and nothing about you.'

There was a moment's silence, as though he was weighing up his answer, and she shot him a curious look.

'I'm in films.'

'In films . . . you're an actor!'

Surprise tinged her voice, flared briefly in the depths of her eyes, and quickly she turned away to hide her incredulous expression. Somehow acting seemed such an unlikely occupation for him; there was a toughness to Rick Dawson, a hint of steel which seemed to sit oddly with her idea of an actor.

'You seem surprised,' he said softly, a strange inflection to his voice which she found hard to interpret.

'Yes, if you must know. I guess I had you down as something rather different,' she answered briefly.

'Mmm, well, I don't think I'll go into just what that might be. I've a feeling I mightn't like the answer,' he said with a slow grin. Harriet smiled back, silently admitting he could be right. Somehow 'actor' seemed too tame an occupation for a man like Rick Dawson. Still, the idea intrigued her, and there was more than a hint of curiosity in her voice when she spoke.

'What have you been in? Anything I might have heard of?'

Swiftly her eyes ran over the lean contours of his face, and just for an instant she wondered if there wasn't something familiar about the clean-cut curve of brow and angular cheekbone, before quickly she pushed the idea aside as being purely fanciful. If Rick Dawson was an actor of any repute, then she would have heard his name, surely?

'I doubt it,' he answered shortly and for a moment Harriet wondered at his obvious reluctance to go into detail, until suddenly it struck her that he might feel embarrassed by his lack of fame. She had the feeling that being successful would be important to a man like him, the sort of man who would want to be right at the top, no matter where his interests lay. She couldn't imagine him taking kindly to being at the very bottom of the ladder. Still, the fact that he'd obviously not yet made much headway in his chosen profession only emphasised what a bitter blow it must have been to lose his wallet, and she chose her next words carefully.

'About your wallet—I don't want to be nosey, but how will you manage?'

There was a tiny silence, then he said quietly, 'Oh, I'm sure I'll scrape through somehow.'

'Are you certain? I mean, well...what I'm trying to say is that I'd be glad to let you have some cash if you're stuck.'

There was a moment's deep, intense silence, and Harriet felt her face begin to flame as she realised he must have been offended by her offer. Turning her head, she said quickly, 'Look, I'm sorry, I shouldn't have said anything. Please forget I ever...'

Rick leant over and laid a gentle finger against her lips, damming the tumbling fall of words.

'Harriet, honey, it was the nicest thing you could have said. Thank you.'

He pressed a gentle kiss to the curve of her cheek, his lips lingering against the warm, soft skin for just an instant before he drew away, and Harriet felt the blush which tinged her cheeks flood in a warm tide right down to her toes. Gripping the steering wheel tightly, she stared grimly through the windscreen at the grey, unfurling curl of roadway...and tried desperately to remember just how much she still disliked him!

CHAPTER FOUR

An hour or so later it was far easier. In fact, Harriet knew with absolute certainty that if she had to listen to one more crack about her navigating, then she would probably brain him! Oh, perhaps there was a certain justification for a few mild rebukes or a few pithy comments, but nothing could justify the flood of scathing remarks which flowed from his lips. She thrust the map into his hands and said sharply to stem the tide, 'Here, then, Mr Super Navigator. If you think you can do better, then you have a go!'

Folding her arms across her temper-heaving bosom, she leant back and stared grimly out of the window at the grey and streaming sky. It had been raining for a good half-hour now, and driving on the slick roadways had become quite hazardous, demanding all her concentration so that it was little wonder she must have missed the turning, though honesty forced her to admit she probably wouldn't have if she'd paid more attention to Pat's instructions. What on earth was it she'd told her about that crossroads? Harriet racked her brains, trying to remember, but it was useless. Her thoughts at that time had been centred on something else entirely, namely the ungrateful wretch muttering at her side. In fact, if you took it all to its logical conclusion, then this was probably all his fault for distracting her in the first place . . . not that she held out any hope that he'd admit it! Glancing sideways, she raised a slim brow and said sweetly, 'Well, then, have you got it all figured out?'

Raising his head, he glowered at her for a brief moment, green eyes alight with irritation.

'I'd have more chance of figuring it out if you gave me a clue to just where we are, lady, wouldn't I?'

'If I knew where we are, then I wouldn't need to ask you, would I?' she stated with a cold and frosty logic. 'I'd just follow the map as I have been doing for the past three hours.'

'If you'd been following the map, then we wouldn't be lost,' he snapped back. 'Now, come on, take another look and just try and work out where we are.'

He pushed the folded map under her nose, and Harriet looked down at it gloomily for several long, blank seconds. As far as she was concerned she'd followed the red-inked route to the inch, but the fact that they'd found no sign of the campsite yet seemed to indicate she must have slipped a fraction. Now, by her admittedly vague reckoning, they could be on any one of at least three roads, but the trouble was she just couldn't pinpoint which exactly. Looking round, she cast despairing eyes over the dripping hedges which lined the narrow lane, but could find nothing which could give her a clue and save her from any more of his cutting comments. She steeled herself as she said curtly, 'I'm afraid I've absolutely no idea where we are.'

'Oh, great, that's really great. So just where do you suggest we go from here?' he asked harshly, settling back in his seat with a force which made poor Betsy shudder.

'Back?' Harriet suggested, trying hard not to give in to her own rising irritation and snap. OK, so she was at fault for getting them lost, she'd admit it, but did he have to be so rotten about it? A gentleman would surely have handled the situation with a little more finesse and sympathy, but then 'gentleman' wasn't the word she'd use to describe Rick Dawson, was it? For a few comforting seconds Harriet gave herself up to the sheer pleasure of listing names for her travelling companion in a strict alphabetical order, only giving up when she reached 'S' and decided 'skunk' was absolutely perfect!

'Oh, come on, what's the point in going back?' he demanded, interrupting her pleasant little interlude. 'There's nothing there apart from a handful of houses some twenty miles back, is there? No, we'd better go on, and hope we can find some sort of signpost to guide us.'

For a moment Harriet considered arguing with the decision, preferring to return to the small hamlet and ask directions, but one look at his set, uncompromising expression soon convinced her not to bother, and she re-started the engine aggressively. After all, who was she to argue. She was only the poor, tired driver.

Thrusting the car into gear, she set off, following the road as it dipped down into a hollow overhung with trees. Although it was barely mid-afternoon, the sky was so heavy and overcast that little light penetrated the thick matted foliage, and Harriet had to flick on her headlights so that she could see well enough to follow the roadway. It was an eerie feeling, moving down into the green-tinged darkness, and she breathed a soft sigh of relief when they started to climb up the other side of the dip, a sigh which was abruptly cut off as the car started to cough with an asthmatic fervour. Quickly she gunned the engine, her foot pressed nearly to the floorboards in an attempt to gain more power, but it was hopeless. With one last, despairing splutter and one final wheeze, the engine died and slowly the car ground to a gentle halt before starting to slide back down into the hollow. Stamping on the brakes, Harriet stopped the descent and stared at the steering wheel in utter confusion. What on earth had happened? The hill was steep, granted, but surely not that steep that it was beyond the old car's capabilities? Flicking the ignition, she attempted to re-start the engine, but could gain no response other than a thin, metallic whine.

'I wouldn't bother if I was you.'

'Mmm?' Harriet barely spared him a glance, her whole attention centred on the car and its problem. Maybe there was a loose wire, a touch of damp on the plugs; maybe…

'Gas,' he said succinctly. 'You've run out of gas.'

There was a blank split second while her brain did a lightning translation of the statement, then her eyes raced to the petrol gauge and widened in unbelieving horror as she realised he was right and it was registering empty. How could it have happened? She'd filled the tank to the very brim that morning, and worked out that she would have plenty to cover the journey, plus quite a bit over, so how on earth could it be empty? Then the whole unpalatable truth struck her and she groaned in dismay; by getting lost, driving all these miles out of their way, she must have used up all she'd allowed for, plus the extra she'd added as insurance.

'Here, give me the keys. There's no point in you getting wet.' Rick held out his hand, and Harriet stared down at it in utter confusion. What was he on about? What did he need the keys for? Did he know some miraculous way to make the car go without petrol? For a moment hope flared briefly through her, to be snuffed out the instant she heard his next words.

'Come on, I'll get the spare can out of the back and fill her up, then we can get on our way. It'll be midnight before we get there at this rate.'

And for the first time in her entire life Harriet knew what it was to pray for the ground to open up and swallow her. Dipping her head, she stared down at the long, lean fingers and said softly but very clearly, 'It's empty.'

'I know it's empty, honey. That's why I need to get the spare can out of the trunk.'

He spoke just as slowly, just as clearly, but with a hint of strained patience which Harriet had the suspicion was going to be strained even further within the next thirty seconds. Taking a deep breath, she forced herself to look up and meet his eyes, refusing to be viewed as a coward in what she knew might be her last breathing second.

'The can . . . it's empty. I didn't think I'd need to fill it for the journey.'

There was an instant's pause, a tiny fraction of calm before the storm exploded around her, and she flinched back from the typhoon of words which assailed her.

'Empty? Empty? My God, woman, are you trying to tell me that you've set out on this journey without filling up the spare can? No one, but no one could be that stupid, not even you!'

That stung. She could well appreciate he might be annoyed, but he still had no right to start hurling insults at her. She sat up rigidly straight in the seat and refused to answer, staring straight ahead through the rain-misted windscreen, her mouth set in a mutinous line. There was silence in the car, a deep, heavy, ominous silence broken only by the clattering of rain on the roof and the sound of his agitated breathing. Now that her eyes were becoming accustomed to the green gloom, Harriet could see more of where they were parked, but none of it was encouraging. The low hedgerows had petered out yards back, and the narrow lane was rimmed only by the thick trunks of trees which arched overhead. Through a narrow gap between their trunks she could see water-logged fields leading down to an expanse of grey-brown water which must be a river, though it was running so high that it was hard to see just where the land ended and the water began. Another few hours of this downpour, and by the look of it the fields would be flooded. Beyond the river was more open, flat country, more endless wet fields and rain-sodden trees, and nothing at all which could help them. From the look of it the car couldn't have found a worse place to stop, and Harriet bit back a small chuckle of nervous laughter as she realised it.

'I can't really see what you can find to laugh at in all this.' The frosty voice wiped away all traces of her laughter, and Harriet turned towards him, a hint of apology showing briefly on her face.

'I'm sorry. I know it's not really funny, but isn't it typical that whenever you break down it has to be in the middle of nowhere?'

'We haven't broken down. *You've* run out of gas,' he said coldly, and Harriet froze at his tone. Of all the times for it to happen it had to be now, with him in the car, didn't it? Still, there was little point sitting dwelling on the fact; what she had to do now was find some way of getting them out of this mess, and that meant finding some petrol. She opened the door and started to get out, stopping abruptly as he caught her arm in a harsh grasp.

'And where do you think you're going?' he demanded.

Harriet wrenched her arm free before answering, shivering as a sudden blast of rain flurried into the car.

'To get some petrol, of course.'

'And just where do you propose to find it?' he asked, a touch of sarcasm lacing his deep voice.

'Frankly, I've no idea, but there must be a service station around here somewhere, surely?'

'Listen, honey, you could be walking miles before you come to a gas station, and this is hardly the weather for it, is it?'

'Well, then, what do you suggest we do?' she asked nastily. 'Sit here and wait for the cavalry to rescue us?'

'Hardly. If there are as many horses round here as there's been cars, we could be waiting for ever. No, we'd better see if we can find a house and get help, see if we can get a garage to come out to us with some gas.'

For a moment she hesitated, somehow loath to give in to him too easily, then with a small mental shrug she decided to agree, just to keep what was left of the peace between them. She had the feeling Rick Dawson could be a very formidable adversary.

'All right, we'll try it your way, but I'm still taking the spare can with me, just in case.'

He shrugged, a brief movement of his broad shoulders.

'That's up to you, but don't blame me if you end up lugging it around and get sore arms for no reason. The last place you're likely to find a gas station is along a God-forsaken track like this.'

His reasoning was valid, but there was no way Harriet was going to admit it, and stepping out of the car she hurried round to the back and unlocked the doors, gasping at the cold sting of rain which soaked rapidly into her thin lemon sweatshirt. Reaching inside, she pulled out the old nylon jacket she always kept tossed in a corner and dragged it on, glad even of the poor protection it offered against the deluge. The sound of the passenger door slamming warned her that Rick Dawson had decided to follow, and she let her eyes skim over his tall figure, quickly noting the way the rain flattened his blond hair to his skull within seconds, making him look even more formidable than ever. For a tiny second unease ran in a cold finger down her spine, and she shivered with a sudden, strange apprehension. To be stranded in such a lonely spot was bad enough, but to be stranded along with him seemed doubly difficult to handle. There was something about him which frankly unnerved her, made her more aware of him as a man than she'd ever been of anyone else before, and she looked down quickly to hide the expression which flared briefly in her eyes, somehow frightened to let him know just how much he disturbed her.

'Ready?' he asked with more than a hint of sarcasm.

She flushed, reaching into the car for the battered two-gallon can, and setting it down at her feet with a noisy clatter. Then she carefully locked the doors before turning back to face him.

'I'm ready, thank you, but how about you? Don't you think you need a jacket?'

'Yes,' he answered, pushing his hands into the pockets of his jeans so that the fabric strained tighter over the well-formed muscles of his thighs. 'But it just so happens that it's packed in my bag, and that's in the back of the trailer.'

'But you're going to get soaked!' Harriet exclaimed in real concern, her eyes racing rapidly over him. Already the shoulders of his sweatshirt had darkened with soaked-up rain water, and patches of it were clinging to his chest as the wet fabric stuck to his bare skin.

'Well, unless you've got a spare coat in there, there's very little I can do about it,' he answered levelly. 'Let's just hope we can find some sort of shelter before I actually drown.' And Harriet felt even more guilty and miserable than she'd felt earlier. True, she'd hoped to give him a little discomfort on the journey, but there was no way she wanted to be responsible for his catching double pneumonia!

'I'm sorry,' she said, staring down at her feet, unable to meet the green eyes which were still studying her with a less than friendly gleam in their depths.

'Mmm, I guess you are, but sorry's not going to do much to change things, is it?'

'No,' she snapped, all guilt dissolving under the heat of a sudden rising irritation. He could at least have made a pretence of accepting her apologies, surely, instead of making her feel even lower than ever? Picking up the can, she stomped round the car and headed up the lane, her back as stiff as a poker. It was the last time she was going to apologise to him . . . ever!

Temper quickened her step, lengthened her stride so that within minutes she'd climbed up out of the hollow and stood panting at the top of the small hill, looking round for any sign of a house, somewhere which could offer them shelter, but there was nothing, nothing but miles of rain-sodden countryside set under a heavy grey sky.

'You sure picked your spot, lady, didn't you?'

Squelching to a halt, Rick stood beside her, so close she could feel the slight shiver which raced through his body. Although it was mid-May, the air was cold, chilled to an unnatural degree by the freak storm.

'Look, you're frozen,' she said quickly. 'Why don't we share the jacket? We could drape it over our heads, and that way it would keep off the worst of the rain.'

Quickly she went to lower the zip, stopping as his hand covered hers, the long fingers icy against even the meagre warmth left in hers.

'No, you leave it on, there's no point in both of us getting drenched to the skin.'

'But...'

'No. Now, come on, Harriet. Don't stand here arguing, let's get going and find some help.'

There seemed little point in pursuing it; if he was determined to act the martyr, who was she to stop him? Pulling her hand free, she set several paces between them before sweeping her gaze around the empty countryside.

'Just where do you suggest we go, then? I can't see any sign of a house round here, can you?'

'No, but there might be something round that next bend, so let's go and check it out.'

'And what if there isn't?'

'Then I suppose we'll just have to go back to the car and wait for someone to come along, after all.'

'But that could take hours!' she wailed. 'We can't just sit in the car doing nothing.'

'Oh, I'm sure we can find something to fill in the time,' he said slowly, his eyes tracing over her with a gleam in their green depths which brought a sudden flush of colour up under her pale, damp-misted skin. There was a moment's silence, then quickly Harriet turned away and marched off along the road, feeling her pulse start to hammer with a sudden unwelcome rhythm as images of her and Rick Dawson 'filling in time' raced into her mind. And the really shocking thing was that, despite all that had passed between them, the idea didn't seem that unpleasant!

It took longer to reach the bend in the road than they'd imagined. Distances were deceptive in the heavy, driving rain, and by the time they finally got there Harriet was feeling exhausted. She'd always prided herself on being fit, making a point of getting regular exercise by taking long walks several times a week, but somehow those gentle, pleasant strolls bore little resemblance to this tiring battle against nature's nastier elements.

A strong wind had risen, blowing the cold rain directly into their faces so that they had to fight every inch of the way, heads bowed under the relentless stream of water. The nylon jacket soon gave up its unequal struggle against the downpour, and Harriet could feel her sweat-shirt sticking to her shoulders where rain had penetrated the seams. Her denim jeans were soaked, the fabric cold and stiff against her legs, chafing the tender inner flesh of her thighs till they felt quite sore with the friction. All in all, Harriet had never felt so miserable in the whole of her life, and it was with gloomy eyes that she finally stopped to survey the landscape.

'Well, we've made it.'

With a mighty effort she managed to summon up just enough strength to move her feet the fraction needed so that she could focus her rain-blinded eyes in Rick Dawson's direction and let them run slowly over him, taking stock of his appearance.

The navy sweatshirt was black with water, moulding the strong muscles of his chest as it clung wetly to his torso. Tiny rivers of water trickled out of its frayed bottom rib and soaked into his jeans, which clung to his long legs like a second loving skin. His hair was slicked to his skull, the soft pale colour darkened to a rich wheaten shade which blended into the rain-gleaming bronze of his face, and Harriet knew without the shadow of a single tiny doubt that she'd never seen a more magnificent sight as he stood there braced against the elements. There was something about his stance, about the pure, raw masculinity of him, which caught at her imagination, and hastily she turned aside, more disturbed by such thoughts than she cared to admit.

A sudden gust of wind caught at her and she rocked back, gasping under its force. Swiftly, he stepped forwards, his arm circling her waist to steady her, and she felt her breath catch at the sudden unexpected contact as her body brushed against his. There was a moment's quiet stillness while the storm raged around them, then he spoke.

'Well, I'd be tempted to stay like this a little longer, honey, if the weather was better, but I really think we should get on.'

And Harriet felt her face flame at the gentle, knowing mockery in his tone. She quickly pulled away, chiding herself for being so foolish as to let Rick Dawson's obvious attractions sway her. She had to remember what he was really like, had to remember, too, what he'd said earlier about viewing her as a challenge, and not play too easily into his more than capable hands. She had the feeling he'd need far less than the proverbial inch to gain the proverbial mile!

Raising her hand, she shielded her face against the downpour and stared round, suddenly desperate to find somewhere which could offer them help. There was no way she wanted to have to return to the car and spend several hours there with only him for company, no way at all. She had the feeling that would be asking for rather more trouble than she could handle!

Turning in a slow, steady circle, she scrutinised the landscape, hope flaring warmly inside her as she caught brief sight of what appeared to be the corner of a house roof behind a thin stand of trees, before a sudden flurry of rain blurred her vision. She flicked the water from her eyes and looked again, smiling in relief as she realised she'd been right. There *was* a house and, by the look of it, it was a bare quarter of a mile away across the fields.

'Look,' she ordered, triumph edging her voice. 'Can you see it? A house behind those trees.'

He turned, his eyes following her pointing finger, and nodded slowly. 'Mmm. I think you're right.'

There was little enthusiasm in his voice, and Harriet shot him a quick look, her lips curved in irritation.

'What's the matter? You don't sound very happy about it.'

'I'm not,' he said flatly.

'Why on earth not? That's what we came for, isn't it…to find a house, some place we could get help? After all, we're hardly out here to take a nice little afternoon stroll.'

He ignored her gibe, his face expressionless as he stared across the flat landscape towards the part hidden building.

'Well,' she demanded, 'what is it you don't like about it?'

'That,' he replied, pointing.

She turned, puzzled, staring across the open country for a few moments, but she could see nothing at all to alarm her; shrugging her slim shoulders, she turned back towards him.

'I'm sorry, but I just can't see what you're on about.'

'The river, Harriet! Haven't you noticed just how high it's running? It's breaking its banks now and starting to flood into the field.'

'So?' she queried, brown eyes flicking over his grim expression. What on earth did the river have to do with anything? To her mind he was just being awkward, was probably put out because he hadn't been the first one to spot the building.

'So that means we're going to have to cross it to get to the house. It's on the other side, in case you hadn't noticed.'

She hadn't, but there was no way she was going to make an issue out of it when really and truly she couldn't see what the problem was. As far as she was concerned it was a house and a house meant people, and people meant help and that was all there was to it. There was no point in standing wasting valuable time debating the merits of its geographical location, and she pushed the wet hair from her eyes as she said coldly, 'Listen, if you think I'm going marching on looking for somewhere else just because you don't want to get your feet wet, then you can think again. I'm going to that house for help, and it's entirely up to you if you come with me.'

She stepped from the tarmac on to the spongy wet grass and headed off in the direction of that tempting sliver of rooftop, resisting with a steely determination the almost overwhelming urge to shoot a look over her shoulder and see if he was following. If he wanted to stand there getting wetter and wetter by the second, then let him, but as far as she was concerned this was the one and only place they'd seen which might offer help, and there was no way she was going to walk past it.

Head bowed against the blasting gusts of rain which stung her face, she walked across the field, feeling her feet sink into the waterlogged ground. As she got closer to the river the ground became softer, the grass scarcely covering the oozing mud which lurked beneath its surface, and Harriet grimaced as she felt some of the slime spill over the sides of her shoes. Moving carefully, she tried to pick a path across the rough ground, stepping from one thick tufted patch to another in an effort to avoid the worst of the disgusting, foul-smelling mixture.

She tiptoed delicately across one particularly large and evil-looking spot, cursing liberally as her foot slipped a fraction and she ended up ankle-deep in slime.

'Need a hand?' a low, taunting voice queried softly, and she jumped, turning rather too quickly in its direction. Instantly she rued her hasty action. There was a moment when she hovered almost on the brink of regaining her balance, then her feet slid from under her and she fell like a puppet with its strings suddenly cut. With a jolt she hit the ground and sat there, stunned, feeling the cold slither of mud seep quickly into the seat of her jeans. There was a moment's silence, broken by the sudden rolling laugh which rumbled from Rick Dawson's lips. Harriet shot him a look which would have made a lesser man tremble.

'I'm so glad you find it funny, Mr Dawson,' she managed to bite out between clenched teeth.

'Oh, I do, honey, I really do. Possibly the funniest thing I've seen in years. If you could have seen your face…it was a picture.' Raising his hand, he wiped tears of laughter from his face, and Harriet turned away to hide her simmering anger. Moving carefully, she edged herself over to a more solid-looking patch of ground and tried to push herself upright, muttering under her breath as her feet lost their grip on the slippery surface and pitched her straight back into the disgusting slime. Mud oozed between her fingers, slithered over her wrists in a cold, clinging tide, and with an expression of pure distaste on her face she wrenched her hands free and wiped them down the front of her jeans, shuddering.

'Here.'

Rick offered her his hand and Harriet studied it for a moment, far more tempted to bite it than accept it! Looking up, she let her eyes run over his face and felt her anger boil into a real live fury as she saw the laughter which still shimmered in his green eyes. It was all his fault she'd fallen and got herself into this mess; if he hadn't come pussyfooting up and startled her, then none of this would ever have happened, and yet he still had the absolute gall to stand there and laugh at her!

'Well, what are you waiting for? A written invitation? Hurry up.'

It was just what she needed, the final spur to make her follow her instincts, and she reached up and let her fingers just brush against his in a limp little hold.

'Oh, for heaven's sake, woman, get a better grip on my hand than that, can't you?' he ordered impatiently, leaning further forwards to grasp her hand in a strong clasp.

It was all she needed, that tiny split second when he was off balance and unwary, and with a lightning speed she took it. Closing her fingers round his, she pulled as hard as she could manage, watching with a comforting, healing sense of glee as he pitched forwards to land on his knees in the cold, cold mud. There was silence while Harriet gave him a chance to better appreciate her actions, then, turning to him, she said sweetly, 'Oh dear, Mr Dawson, I'm sorry...how on earth did that happen? But still, I know you'll probably see the funny side of it, won't you?'

Rolling over, she scrambled to her feet, anxious to set a little more distance between them before all that stunned horror now showing on his face turned to a vengeful anger. In truth, if she'd been sensible, then she should have buried that instinct the moment it broke the surface, but now, scooping mud off the back of her filthy jeans, Harriet knew there was no way she regretted her action. He'd asked for something a little bit special by mocking her so cruelly, and to her mind he'd definitely just got it!

'It just makes me even more determined to win, you know, Miss Prince.'

He'd come up quietly alongside her and she swung round, a trickle of sudden apprehension racing coldly through her as she saw the expression on his face. Forcing herself to an outward show of calmness, she turned and walked stiffly on towards the beckoning rooftop before she answered.

'I'm afraid I don't know what you mean.'

'No?'

He caught hold of her arm and swung her round to face him, holding her gaze for a long second before he raised his hand and gently wiped a smear of mud from off her nose. Slowly his finger traced down the narrow little slope before coming to rest on the soft, parted fullness of her lips, and Harriet felt her heart begin to hammer in a sudden heavy rhythm as she stood there, somehow unable to break free from his light hold.

'I'm talking about the challenge, Miss Prince...surely you haven't forgotten about it already, have you?' he asked gently, and she looked away, unable to meet that glittering emerald gaze for a moment longer.

'No,' she whispered, her voice so low that it barely carried above the sounds of the storm which still raged around them.

'No,' he echoed just as softly. 'No, I didn't think you had.'

Dropping his hand, he moved away, walking unhurriedly in the direction of the house, and Harriet stood as though turned to stone, staring after his tall, powerful figure, till a sudden shiver racked her slender body...a shiver not of cold but of a strange, disconcerting premonition that he might just win! She would have to be careful.

CHAPTER FIVE

THE RIVER was high, its brownish-grey waters swirling in a strong tide which ate into the banks and lapped over into the surrounding fields for several yards on either side. Harriet felt her heart sink as she looked at it. Back on the road it had all seemed so clear-cut and simple; she'd get to the river, wade across, then make her way up to the house and ask for help, but now, actually faced with the reality of the situation, it was a different story.

There was no way she could judge the depth of that murky water, no way she could tell just how high it would come up her body, and not for the first time in her life Harriet rued the fact that she'd never learned to swim. Not that she would have been really tempted to try, even if she could, she had to admit; the river was full of debris, and she could see little attraction in entering that swirling jumble of silt and broken branches. Still, it left her with the problem of what to do next and, turning towards the man at her side, she said briefly, 'Well, what do you think?'

They'd barely exchanged a word for the past few minutes as they'd crossed the field, and Harriet had the unnerving feeling that he wasn't so much seething with frustrated anger as plotting his revenge! However, now was not the time to worry about what he'd come up with, she'd face that where and when it happened, lord help her! Now she had to decide on a course of action which might hopefully get them out of this mess. Should they attempt to cross the river or should they give up and return to the car? Neither was a very tempting prospect, but somehow she felt the river and all its attendant problems held the slightly greater appeal; being trapped in the car with Rick Dawson was a far more dangerous prospect than a mere raging torrent, after all!

'There's no way we can cross here,' he answered after a few minutes' silent study. 'We can't tell how deep it is, and even if we try to swim across it could be dangerous. That's a very strong current running.'

'I can't swim,' she said shortly, somehow loath to admit this failing to him of all people.

'Well, that settles that, then, doesn't it? We'll have to find some other way of getting across. There's probably a bridge further on, so let's go and find it.'

He led the way downstream and Harriet followed, feeling her legs start to tremble with the effort of walking across the marshy ground. She was so tired, tired and wet and hungry, and would have given anything just for the chance to sit down somewhere dry and rest. Still, maybe when they eventually managed to get across to the house she'd get her chance; it was just enough to keep her going.

Picking up the now mud-caked petrol can, she trudged after the tall figure of the American, head bowed and eyes slitted against the driving force of the wind, so that when he stopped suddenly she cannoned into his back and sent him reeling.

'For heavens' sake, woman, can't you look where you're going?'

'Sorry,' she apologised wearily. 'I just didn't see that you'd stopped.'

She cast a glance at the nearby river and her heart did a little leap for joy as she realised just why he'd halted so abruptly. There was a bridge, as he'd so rightly guessed, and at the other side of it, a bare twenty yards distant, she could see what was evidently the back wall of the house. They'd made it! Relief rushed through her and she took a step forwards, anxious to get to the house as soon as she could.

'*Wait!*'

Catching her arm, Rick halted her abruptly, and she stopped dead, her eyes wary as they swung up to his.

'When will you learn to stop and look before you leap?' he said wryly. 'Just take a look at that bridge, will you, honey? Then maybe you'll see why I don't want you rushing across it.'

Annoyed by this rather less than flattering assessment of her character, Harriet spun round and shot a quick glance over the small wooden plank bridge, her spirits sinking as she realised what he meant. The bridge was old, narrow, a low arch of rotting timber which barely skimmed the top of the fast-flowing river. Even as she watched, a small, whirling eddy of muddy water washed over its splintery sides and swirled across the worn boards in a dirty tide.

'It doesn't look too safe, does it?' he said, and she nodded, her voice dejected when she spoke.

'So what shall we do now? It seems such a shame to have to turn back when we've got so close.'

'We're not going back,' he said steadily, pushing the wet hair from his broad, tanned forehead. 'I'll go across and see if I can get someone to help us.'

'And leave me here? No chance! If you go, I go. There's no way I'm going to stand here a moment longer getting soaked,' she retorted hotly, and he shrugged, water scattering from his sweater as he moved his shoulders.

'OK, it's up to you. I was only trying to save you from making the crossing.'

'I'll manage.'

'Fine, but let me go first. If it holds my weight, then there should be no trouble about it holding yours.'

Without waiting for an answer, he stepped carefully on to the bridge, and Harriet held her breath as she heard the ominous creaking of the worn, water-sodden timber. Slowly, carefully, he moved across the narrow arch, pausing as a sudden surge of water and broken branches swamped his feet when he reached the centre. For a second he waited till the water had swilled over the other side, then still moving with that same steady stride he completed the crossing, and Harriet let her pent-up breath flow.

He cupped his hands to his mouth to shout to where she stood quaking on the other bank.

'Take your time and don't lean too much weight on the handrails, they're rotten. And try and stay in the middle.'

Too anxious to speak, Harriet merely nodded before setting her foot gingerly on to the first wooden tread, wincing slightly as the wood groaned under her slight weight. Imitating his slow, careful tread, she inched her way across, gasping as water swirled over her feet well before she'd even reached the middle. The river was rising, by the second if her eyes weren't deceiving her, and with a grim little shudder she wondered just how long it would be before this fragile crossing was swept away. The thought spurred her on, added a fleetness to her tired legs which defied all caution, so that within seconds she stood panting by his side.

'That was one hell of an act, lady,' he said coldly.

He sounded angry, and Harriet studied the thin line of red which edged his cheekbones with startled eyes. What on earth was he so cross about? Surely he hadn't been worried about her, had he? It was a warming thought, one which sent a little curl of pleasure racing through her, and she hurried to reassure him, stopping abruptly when he said harshly, 'Don't you even have enough sense to realise what could have happened if you'd slipped? You'd have been in that water, and I'd have had one hell of a job to get you out!'

And with a little snort of disgust she dismissed the thought as utterly foolish. The only thing that had worried Rick Dawson was the thought that if she'd fallen he might have got wet trying to fish her out! Flicking the sodden hair from her eyes, she stomped her way up the shallow banking, crushing the vegetation underfoot with the same force as he'd just crushed that warm little feeling.

Rounding the corner of the house at a spanking pace, she marched straight up to the green-painted door and hammered loudly on it, huddling into the meagre shelter offered while she waited. There was silence, an ominously echoing silence, and she knocked again, pressing her ear to the wet wood as she listened for any sound of footsteps.

'No answer?'

'No!' she snapped, still too annoyed to bother adding even a measure of politeness. Moving over, she rubbed her hand over the rain-misted glass of a nearby window and peered inside, and felt her tired legs go suddenly weak with disappointment. All the furniture in the room was shrouded in ghostly white dustsheets, proclaiming all too clearly that the house was empty and, from the look of it, had been for some time.

'It's empty,' she stated, her voice flat with disappointment, and he paused, fist raised to hammer on the door.

'Are you sure?'

'Take a look.'

Stepping aside, she let him take her place at the window, leaning back against the stone wall of the house in sudden exhaustion. To think they'd trekked all this way, crossed that damned river, and all for what? To suddenly discover the house was empty... it just wasn't fair.

The sudden sharp sound of glass shattering roused her from her self-pitying misery, and she turned quickly, her eyebrows rising as she caught sight of Rick Dawson's arm half-way inside the broken window-pane.

'What on earth are you doing?' she demanded.

'What does it look like? Getting us out of this storm, of course.'

Twisting his arm upwards, he pulled at the small catch that secured the long, narrow window, and it fell open.

'But you can't do that! You can't just go breaking into people's houses.'

'No? Well, I'm afraid I just have.'

Pushing the window wide, he swung a leg over the sill and started to inch his way in sideways, stopping abruptly as she caught his arm and held him back.

'Rick, that's breaking and entering... it's a criminal offence.'

Perched half in and half out of the small opening, he shrugged his arm free before turning to her, a determined gleam in his eyes.

'Listen, honey, if you want to stand out there waiting for a proper invitation to enter, then it's fine by me, but there's no way I'm going to stand there with you. Be sensible, we're not going to do any damage, just take shelter, maybe see if there's a telephone, that's all. We can always leave some money behind when we go, to pay for the broken pane.'

'Well...' Undecided, Harriet chewed on her bottom lip until the thought of a few precious minutes away from the blasting force of the storm became far too tempting to resist, and she nodded.

'Good girl. Now, you hang on there a second and I'll open the front door for you.'

He patted her cheek before swinging his other leg through the opening and disappearing inside. Harriet walked the few paces to the big, solid door and stood waiting, shivering slightly as the wind roared in great gusts over her soaked body. There was the sound of locks turning, then the door swung open and she hurried inside to stand dripping on the dusty parquet floor. Rick slammed the door shut and a beautiful storm-free silence echoed round the small, dark hallway. Looking round, she took quick stock of the slightly shabby furnishings, her nose twitching at the musty smell of stale air.

'Right then, let's see if there's a phone.'

Feet squelching in their soaked trainers, Rick led the way along the hall and peered into the first room, a small sound of satisfaction leaving his lips as he spotted the black telephone perched on a fragile-looking dark wood table. Crossing the room in two long strides, he picked up the receiver and pressed it to his ear for several seconds before turning to her, his face grim.

'It's dead,' he stated shortly.

'What do you mean?'

Uncaring that she was tracking muddy footprints across the pale flowered carpet, Harriet hurried to his side and snatched the receiver from him. Pressing it to her ear, she rattled the buttons on the base several times, then waited for the dialling tone to start, but there was nothing but a complete and total silence. Slowly she set it back down.

'Now what do we do?' she asked quietly.

'There's not a lot we can do, is there? We'll have to spend the night here, then start off again in the morning and see if we can find somewhere else.'

'Spend the night . . . here?' she croaked, her eyes huge in the paleness of her face. 'We can't do that!'

'Why not?' he asked, a mocking curve to his lips as he studied her face. 'To my mind, it's the only sensible thing we can do. After all, we'll be out of the storm, dry . . . fairly comfortable, and we might even find something to eat if there's anything left in the cupboards. So we may as well make the most of it.'

Reaching up, he pulled the sodden sweater over his head, and Harriet felt her breath catch in sudden panic as she caught sight of his tanned flesh gleaming bronze in the dim light which filtered through the window. Suddenly the room seemed overpoweringly small and cramped, as though she'd accidentally spilled some of Alice's Wonderland liquid and everything had started to shrink, and slowly, carefully, she took a step backwards. There was no way she could spend the night here in this house with Rick Dawson, no way at all. It was a situation she just wasn't prepared for, and couldn't handle. She had to get away, get back to the car . . . anywhere but spend the next few hours here in his disturbing company. She strode briskly from the room and along the hall, pausing fractionally as he called to her.

'Where the hell are you going?'

'Back to the car,' she snapped.

Wrenching the door open, she staggered back a pace under the force of the wind, her heart leaping when he caught her arm in a harsh grip and swung her round.

'Don't be so stupid, woman. What's the point in going back to the car? It won't start without petrol, and as far as I know you've not managed to find any.'

Ignoring his sarcasm, Harriet pulled free and strode out of the door, refusing to give him the satisfaction of making her justify her actions. Maybe it was illogical and hasty, but deep down she knew there was no way she wanted to spend the night alone with him.

'Come back here...*now*!!'

It was an order, plain and simple, and the one thing guaranteed to make Harriet, who hated taking orders, even more determined to have her way. Turning the corner of the house, she strode quickly towards the bridge, just the tiniest flicker of alarm running through her as she realised the water had risen even in the short time since they'd crossed it. Still, she'd done it once, so there was absolutely no reason why she couldn't do it a second time, was there? Carefully using the same measured tread she'd seen him use, she began the crossing.

'Come back, you little fool!' he roared, anger and more than a hint of some other emotion in his voice, but she ignored it, too intent on getting to the other side. There was a slight sway to the bridge now, a feeling of fragility, and she held her breath as she inched her way across, letting it out softly as she passed the half-way mark and started down the last few yards. She'd made it!

Suddenly water swilled over the boards in a dragging surge, catching at her feet so that for an instant she staggered and grasped the handrail. There was a terrible creaking groan of wood tearing from wood; then, as though it was happening in slow motion, she felt herself start to fall sideways.

'*Harriet!*'

There was a tiny split second when she had time to wonder at the real terror in his voice as he called her name, then she hit the water and sank. Water filled her nose, her mouth, her ears, so that she felt her head would burst with the pressure of it, then slowly, mercifully, everything went dark...as dark as the river which closed over her limp body.

She came to slowly, forcing her heavy lids open and wincing as the pale dim light made them burn. Her head ached, a dull, throbbing ache deep inside her skull which made her frightened to move too quickly. Her mouth was dry and, swallowing hard, she tried to find some moisture to wet it, groaning as pain stabbed at her throat. What had happened? Why did she feel so dreadful? Was she ill?

'Here, sip this.'

A strong hand raised her head a fraction, and she sipped thankfully at the cool fruit juice for a few seconds before raising her eyes to the face hovering above hers...and suddenly it all slid back into place. Panic raced through her, caught at her breath, flared in the depths of her dark eyes, and with a low, muttered curse he set the glass abruptly down on the bedside-table and gripped her firmly by the shoulders so that she winced at the sudden pain.

'Stop it!' he ordered, his voice grim. 'Just stop it now. You're quite safe. It's all over.'

She stared up at him, memories of those terrible few seconds when she'd hit the water racing through her, and with a murmur he forced her head round so that their eyes met and Harriet felt all the panic slowly start to fade. He was right; it was all over and she was safe.

'That's better,' he said softly, sitting down on the side of the bed so that the soft mattress tilted, rolling her body against the hard, firm length of his thigh. Picking up her hand, he held it gently in his, and she was surprised to feel the slight tremble which coursed through his long, hard fingers. For a moment he was silent, then when he spoke his voice was rough-edged with emotion.

'I don't think I'll ever forget that look of terror on your face when you fell into the river till the day I die.'

There was no mistaking that his distress was genuine, and she covered his hand with hers, her fingers cold against his flesh.

'I'm sorry,' she said, her voice strained and husky. 'It was a stupid, senseless thing to do. I...I just don't know what came over me.'

'No?' he murmured, his eyes finding and holding hers, and Harriet felt her cheeks flood with betraying colour and turned away. It was a lie and they both knew it, both knew just why she'd fled, but there was no way she was going to admit it. It made her far too vulnerable.

He pushed the damp, dishevelled hair from her forehead, his hand gentle against her skin, and Harriet shivered, her eyes flicking round to meet his. He smiled, a slow, sensuous smile which made the blood start to flow a little more warmly through her veins.

'I think we both know why you did it, honey, but don't worry, I'm not going to push it. I just want you to know one thing; when we make love, it will be with your full co-operation, Harriet, nothing less.'

'When we make...now, you look here, Rick Dawson, don't you think you're being just a little...?'

Outraged, she tried to push herself upright, groaning as the room suddenly started to tilt and spin out of focus. Leaning back, she rested limply against the mound of pillows, suddenly too weak to continue her tirade.

'Now, don't excite yourself,' he said gently, a teasing note to his deep, soft voice. 'We don't want you making yourself sick again, do we? You've already done enough of that for one day.'

And Harriet closed her eyes in mortification. How had it all happened? How had her well-ordered and nicely regimented life changed so abruptly in such a short space of time? There had to be some sort of reason for it, and deep down she had the nastiest feeling she knew just what it was—all six foot of it. Ever since she'd come back and found Rick Dawson in the back of the taxi, her life had been in turmoil, and, from the look of it, it was going from bad to even worse. Where on earth would it all end—that was what really bothered her— just where?

'Well, if you're sure you're OK, I'll leave you to get some sleep. You probably need it.'

Easing himself up from the side of the bed, Rick stared down at her for a brief moment, the soft light from the oil lamp casting a silvery glow over his blond hair. Suddenly Harriet realised there was one very important thing which she'd forgotten, but which must be said. Reaching out, she caught his hand and held it.

'Rick—thank you.'

'What for?'

'Why, for saving me, of course. I owe you.'

He smiled, his eyes crinkling at the corners with a gentle humour which edged the harshness from his face.

'I'll remind you of that, honey, when I come to collect.'

He gently tucked her hand back into the covers, then walked quietly from the room and closed the door, leaving his words to echo round the silence and lull her into a deep, dream-filled sleep.

CHAPTER SIX

A GREY morning light poured in through the window, and Harriet stretched, groaning as her ribs ached in protest. The whole of her mid-section felt sore and tender, and just for a moment she wondered what she'd done, till it came to her that it had probably needed some quite forceful action to pump the river out of her lungs, and a sudden shiver raced down her spine. She'd been lucky; if Rick hadn't followed her, hadn't seen her fall, then she'd be dead. He'd saved her life, and there was no way she could ever repay him for such a debt. It was a disturbing thought.

Tossing back the bedclothes, she forced herself out of the warm bed and stood up, swaying slightly as her head spun with a momentary dizziness. Then she slowly crossed the room and pushed back the folds of the dusty floral curtains to peer out of the window . . . and gasped aloud in stunned amazement.

Water! Water everywhere, covering the fields, the hedges, the road, in a flat, unmoving leaden sea, broken only by islets of trees, their green foliage the only spots of colour against the grey tide. And right in the middle of it all was this house! They were trapped!

She went to rush from the room to find Rick and wake him, let him know just what had happened, but stopped abruptly as she caught sight of herself in the dusty, spotted mirror fixed to the wall. Slowly her eyes slid over her reflection, studying the thin, almost transparent cotton shirt she was wearing with blank amazement.

Whose was it? Where had it come from? More importantly, how did she come to be wearing such a garment?
She didn't remember putting it on. Steadily her gaze
skimmed up the long, slender bare length of her legs to
where the cotton skimmed her thighs, then upwards to
the full swell of her breasts clearly outlined through the
fine fabric, and halted. She'd never seen the shirt before,
so just where had it come from?

The door opened and she swung round, startled, her
eyes racing to the man who stood framed in the doorway.

'So, I see you're awake at last,' he said calmly, his
eyes skimming over her from head to toe, 'but I think
you'd better put something warmer on or you'll catch
a chill. I've left some clothes for you on the end of the
bed.'

And Harriet felt the colour race under her skin in a
sudden scalding tide. She snatched up the end of the
bedcover and wound it round her body, ignoring the deliberate mocking tilt of his dark eyebrows. When she
spoke, her voice was low but filled with anger.

'Did you dress me in this?'

'Of course,' he answered easily, leaning carelessly
against the door-frame.

'How dare you, how dare you undress me?' she
snapped, her eyes spitting. 'What right had you to do
such a thing?'

'The right I earned by jumping into the river and
saving you, lady, that's what. Listen, before you start
getting everything out of context as you seem so prone
to do, when I pulled you from that river you were half
drowned and frozen. There was no way I could have left
you in wet clothes all night, or you'd have probably
caught pneumonia. Yes, I stripped you and dried you
and dressed you, but it was all for your own good, not

for some voyeuristic pleasure. I've seen naked women before, and one more body's hardly going to incite me to an uncontrollable passion, so get that into your dumb little head!'

He strode from the room, slamming the door behind him with such force it made the whole room quiver, and Harriet sat down, stunned into unthinking silence till slowly common sense returned. Of course he'd had to undress her and get her out of her wet clothing, or cold might have done what the river had failed to: kill her. She'd been a fool to make so much of it, a fool and an ungrateful one at that. That man had risked his life saving her, and what had she done to reward him? Nothing but chew him out. She'd have to apologise for it, now.

She stripped off the shirt, shivering as the damp cold penetrated her naked body, and, snatching up the bundle of clothes from the end of the bed, sorted quickly through them. They were all clean, and for that, at least, she had to be grateful, but the style! Holding up a voluminous print dress, Harriet stifled a chuckle as she realised the last time she'd seen anything like it had been in a glass case in a museum! The clothes were obviously originals dating from some time in the mid-fifties, and just for a moment she wondered why Rick had chosen them, unless it had been for some sort of joke. There had to be something more suitable, surely?

She swung open the narrow door of the dusty wardrobe and pulled out a handful of garments to spread them out on the bed. However, one swift look at the floral prints with their tucked sleeves and prim collars soon convinced her she'd done him a disservice; from the look of it he'd picked the cream from the selection, so she might as well set her mind to it and get dressed.

She pulled on a pair of cotton panties, so large they'd have cut down into two pairs of her usual bikini briefs, but, after just one glance at the beige-pink bra that lay in the neat pile of folded clothing, tossed it aside with a shudder. There was no way she was going to entrust her bosom to that contraption of whalebone and stiffening, no way at all. As far as she was concerned, it should be relegated to the torture department of the nearest dungeon!

Within minutes she was dressed and, moving back to the mirror, ran a glance over her new reflection, her lips curving into an amused smile at the sight of the strange apparition which stared back at her. From the top of her damp-frizzed hair to the tips of her bare toes she looked dreadful; there was just no other word for it. Still, one thing was certain: she need have no worries that her appearance would incite anyone to sudden passion!

The thought reminded her all too sharply of what had happened, and she sobered, bending to thrust her feet into a pair of checked slippers she'd found by the side of the bed. They were rather large but she kept them on, preferring a little discomfort to the feel of the cold lino under her feet. From the look of this room and from what she remembered of the downstairs yesterday, the whole house seemed to have been caught in some strange time-warp, as though all the clocks had suddenly stopped in the fifties and never started to tick again, and just for a moment she wondered about the owners, before pushing the thought quickly away. There'd be time enough to worry what they would say about this unscheduled occupation of the house later; now there were more pressing matters to attend to.

She opened the door and stepped out, moving quietly along the landing to the head of the stairs and stopping abruptly as she caught sight of the water which lapped at the bottom treads. From the look of it, the downstairs rooms must be flooded, and for a moment a tiny flicker of panic raced through her, a ghost of yesterday's frightening experience, till briskly she shrugged it aside. There was no way the water could rise any further and reach the very top of the stairs; the house was built at the top of a shallow slope, so that now the rain had stopped there would be little chance that the river would rise any higher, and it was just stupid and pointless to worry about it.

Turning away from the sight of the scummy water, she hesitated, suddenly conscious of the silence which seemed to echo round the house, and her hand grasped the smooth wooden rail of the banister as another sharper fear attacked her. Why was it so quiet, so very silent? Where was Rick? What was he doing? Surely he'd not been so angry at what she'd said that he'd left her, had he? It wasn't a pleasant thought, and her knuckles whitened as she gripped the rail a little tighter, her ears straining for any sound of movement, her body so tense that when a small noise came from along the landing she jumped and swung round towards it.

'Rick?'

There was a tremulous note to her voice as she called his name, her breath whispering into the silence in a sigh of relief when he answered.

'Here...in the bathroom.'

She walked along the corridor, on legs that suddenly felt strangely weak, peering in through several open doors till she spotted the edge of the bath. It was galling to have to admit it, but whereas yesterday the thought of being alone with him had been the frightening prospect, the thought of now being alone *without* him was doubly dreadful! In a mere twenty-four hours she'd come to rely on him, more than she'd realised, and far more than she cared to acknowledge.

She walked into the room, her face smoothed carefully blank to hide this sudden startling revelation, but one look at the tall figure hunched over the basin soon chased the blankness away.

'Rick, what is it?'

She hurried to his side, her eyes sweeping over his pain-etched features, fast noting the pallor which lay waxenly under his tan. She went to grasp his arm, frightened that he was going to fall, but stopped as he flinched away with a low, hoarse murmur. Harriet stared at him, completely puzzled; what was wrong? He'd seemed all right earlier, so what had happened in the past ten minutes since he'd left her?

There was a smell in the room, a trace of something which lingered in the depths of her memory, and she stared at the spilled bottle of dark liquid lying in the basin. She picked it up to study the label, her brow puckering in confusion. Iodine . . . what on earth had he been doing with that?

She ran her eyes over his naked torso and felt her blood turn cold at the sight of the ugly wound which marred the smooth, tanned flesh below his ribs on his left side. Bile rose in a bitter wave in her throat, and she swallowed hard to force it down, knowing she'd be absolutely no help to him if she gave in to the sudden wave of sickness. For the moment her feelings had to take second place to the fact he desperately needed help. She soon realised that apart from the closed lid of the toilet there was nowhere else for him to sit down, but it would have to do.

There was no way she could take a chance on trying to get him somewhere more comfortable; if he passed out she'd never be able to lift him, he was far too heavy.

Moving cautiously in the confined space, she edged herself round, careful not to brush against the purpling flesh, and grasped his arm, winding it firmly across the narrow width of her shoulders.

'Listen, Rick,' she said, forcing a calmness to her voice she was far from feeling. 'I'm just going to help you over to the toilet so you can sit down. Do you think you can make it?'

He nodded, with the briefest movement of his blond head, and Harriet knew she dared not wait a minute longer. There was a greyness to his face now, a beading of perspiration across his forehead which proclaimed all too clearly that there were only seconds left before he might pass out. Carefully she guided him round, her legs sagging as she felt his weight pressing hard on her shoulders. It was only three steps across the room, but to Harriet it felt like thirty, as his legs started to buckle under him and she took almost the full weight of his big frame. Gritting her teeth, she held him upright, her body quivering with the effort, then steadied him as he sat slowly down.

'Put your head down, between your knees,' she ordered grimly, pressing her hand to the nape of his neck so that he was forced to bend forwards, too weak to disobey.

It took several minutes before Harriet could see the frightening pallor start to ease from his face, and she felt relief race through her in a trembling tide. For a few moments there she'd felt certain he would pass out completely, but somehow, by some sort of superhuman effort, he'd managed to hang on to his senses and fight

off the attack. Checking that he was steady enough to
support himself for a moment, she moved away and
dipped a flannel in cold water, kneeling down at his feet
to wipe it over his face, pausing as the green eyes flickered
open and stared into hers.

'Are you all right?' she murmured softly.

'Yes...I think so.'

His voice was low and husky, and she went once more
to the basin and ran water into a mug, too concerned
with how he was feeling to be overly choosy about its
chipped state. Handing it to him, she watched as he
sipped and swallowed the cold liquid before saying
quietly, 'Now, how about telling me just what happened, and more importantly how you got that gash?'

She ran her eyes swiftly over the wound, then looked
away, her stomach still not equal to the sight.

'I just felt faint,' he replied shortly, staring down into
the mug still clasped in his long-fingered hands.

'So I gathered, but why? Look, Rick, that's a terrible
cut you've got there, so how did you do it?'

He hesitated, as though reluctant to tell her, and
Harriet's lips snapped shut like a gin-trap. Folding her
arms across her bosom, she stared down at him, determined to wait all day if need be till she got her answer,
and after one swift glance at her set expression he
conceded defeat.

'A piece of log hit me last night when I went in the
river after you; it must have cut my side, but I hadn't
realised it was so bad till now.'

'And the iodine...what were you doing with that?'

'I reckoned I'd better try and clean it up a bit as I
didn't get the chance last night. The iodine was all I could
find, so I poured it over.'

'You poured it over a cut like that? No wonder you went faint, it must have hurt like hell!'

She picked the discarded wash-cloth off the floor and rinsed it out, needing a few moments to get her feelings into some kind of order, though nothing could assuage the wave of guilt which filled her. He'd been hurt saving her, and there was no way she could ignore that fact, no way that she could deny it was all her fault. If she hadn't gone rushing off like some hysterical virgin, then he would never have had to jump into the river to save her, and ended up with an injury like that for his efforts! When she'd said last night that she owed him, she'd had no idea just how much!

A sudden movement in her side vision made her swing round, her eyes racing to Rick, who was trying to lever himself to his feet; with a few quick strides she crossed the room and pushed him back down.

'And just where do you think you're going?' she demanded.

'To finish getting dressed,' he snapped back with equal vigour.

'Oh, no, you're not.'

'No?' Raising a quizzical eyebrow, he ran a glance over her slender figure. 'And why not, may I ask, unless you've got something planned which needs me near naked?'

Ignoring this deliberate provocation, Harriet held on to her temper and pinned him with a firm stare and her most headmistressy expression.

'The only thing I've got planned, Rick Dawson, is cleaning that cut. Heaven knows what's in that river water, but you can be certain there's nothing healthy. Now, you just sit there while I find something to cover it with.'

'Yes, ma'am.'

With a mocking salute he leant back against the cream-painted wall, folding his arms across his bare chest, and Harriet felt her cheeks fill with a sudden rush of colour and turned away. Pulling open the door of a rusting wall-mounted medicine cabinet, she rifled quickly through it, trying to keep her mind rigidly on the task and away from all those strong, tanned muscles. She'd seen near-naked men before, so it was quite ridiculous to let the sight of one more disconcert her.

There was little in the cabinet apart from a handful of grimy lint and a small pair of rusty scissors, so, with a quick glance to check he wasn't moving, she hurried back down the landing to the room she'd slept in and pulled open the dresser drawers to search quickly through them till she found a clean white cotton petticoat. She held it up and ran assessing eyes over it, pleased to see that it was as generously cut as all the other clothing and should be perfect for bandages. Within the space of a few minutes she was back in the bathroom, picking at the seams of the garment so she could start to tear it apart.

'Mmm, now, in all the movies I've seen, the heroine usually strips off her own underwear to make bandages,' he said drily, and she gave him a cold stare, her hands busy.

'This heroine hasn't got enough underwear to spare,' she answered shortly, 'so I'm afraid this is the best she can do. Now, hold still while I bathe that cut.'

She soaked a strip of folded material in water and some of the diluted iodine, then gently wiped round the edges of the cut, feeling the way his skin shivered at the contact with the antiseptic.

'All right?' she asked softly, concern filling her brown eyes as she felt the rigidity of his body. She hated to hurt him, but it had to be done otherwise there was a very real danger of infection setting in.

'Yes,' he answered tautly.

Working as gently as possible, she cleaned the wound till she was satisfied there was no more dirt in it, then tossed the soiled cloth aside. Taking another portion of cotton, she folded it into a pad big enough to cover the whole of the damaged area and held it lightly against him, her fingers barely brushing against his damp skin.

'Now, hold that in place for a second while I make a bandage,' she instructed, and he nodded, his hand inching under hers to hold the dressing in place.

She quickly cut into the rest of the petticoat, then ripped it into lengths and knotted them together as a makeshift bandage.

'I must say I'm very impressed by all this,' he said quietly, his eyes following her steady movements. 'I didn't know you could add nursing to all your other talents.'

'Three weeks ago I couldn't have,' she answered, rolling the uneven strip of cloth to make it easier to handle.

'Why, what happened three weeks ago?'

'I took a first-aid course.'

'And I'm your first patient?'

'Yes, and hopefully my last. I've a feeling I'm not cut out for nursing. Now just move your arm up a fraction. Right, that's fine, but hold still, I'm a novice at this.'

She started to unwind the bandage round his lower chest, leaning forwards so that her face brushed against the hard bones of his shoulder as she reached round behind him to pass the cloth from left to right. She could feel the heat of his skin against her cheek, smell the faint musky smell of his body, and suddenly her pulse started to pick up its beat. There was something disturbing about being so close to him, about touching him in such an intimate way, her hands sliding over the smooth muscle and bone in a gentle movement which was more like a caress than anything, and she searched desperately for something to say to cover her feelings.

'Pat suggested that I went on the course, so you've got her to thank, really. She felt it would be helpful if I had a basic idea of what to do in case of any accidents on camp, though of course both she and Ted hold first-aid certificates.'

'I see—well, I must say I am grateful, both to her and to you.'

'To me? I'd have thought the last person you needed to be grateful to was me. I mean, if I hadn't gone dashing off like that, then you'd never have been injured, would you?'

Harriet drew back a fraction, her face gently flushed, her dark eyes mirroring her guilt as she stared up into his face.

'I'm really sorry, Rick, about yesterday and what ... what I said to you earlier.'

'Are you?'

He took the end of the cloth out of her hand and tucked it in to secure the bandage, his green eyes holding hers with an expression in them which made her heart beat even faster.

'How about showing me just how sorry you are, honey?' he asked softly.

Leaning forwards, he lessened the distance between them so that his mouth was just a bare inch from hers and waited, waited for the answer Harriet knew she must give him. Slowly, gently, she moved forwards till her lips met his in the lightest, sweetest of kisses, feeling the tremor which poured through her like wine at the touch of his firm, cool lips. Then she pulled back and looked down, unable to meet that brilliant, discerning green gaze while she was still so very vulnerable. Her head was spinning, whirling with a hundred feelings she didn't understand and didn't think she wanted to at the moment. All she knew was that she would remember that brief, gentle kiss for ever.

'Friends?' he asked, his low voice soft and gently teasing, and she looked up, her face flushed and filled with a confusion she could no longer hide.

'Yes,' she murmured. 'Friends.' And desperately prayed it was nothing more than friendship which filled her with such a warm rush of feeling!

The rest of the morning passed in a harmony Harriet wouldn't have believed possible just twenty-four hours earlier, as they worked side by side trying to make themselves comfortable in one of the empty bedrooms. Evidently Rick had had some idea that the house could flood, so after he'd left her to sleep the night before had moved some things which they might need upstairs, including one very important item, an old methylated spirit stove he'd found in the back of one of the kitchen cupboards. While Harriet arranged things as best she could in the small room, he worked on the stove, stripping it down and cleaning out the rusted burners with an old toothbrush and some of the lint they'd found in the bathroom.

It took the best part of an hour, but finally he got it working and set a pan of water on to boil for a much-needed drink, while Harriet checked through their food supplies. There had not been much left in the kitchen cupboards, and some of the packets she discarded immediately after one brief glance at their poor condition. However, there were several tins which seemed undamaged, and, though their diet promised to be sparse for the next few days, at least they wouldn't starve, or rather, they wouldn't if she managed to find a can opener, which seemed to be the one vital item missing.

Leaving Rick to watch over the stove, she ventured downstairs, her nose wrinkling in distaste at the pungent smell from the scummy water which reached almost to her knees. Tucking the full skirt of the cotton dress up to keep it dry, she paddled her way along the hall, her bare toes flinching away from the small mounds of pebbles and soil which had washed in with the flood water. Crossing the kitchen, she hunted quickly through the old cabinets next to the stone sink till she found an ancient can opener and a few pieces of cutlery which might just come in useful.

'Are you all right?'

The deep voice came from the direction of the stairwell, and Harriet started back towards it as she answered, 'Yes, fine. I've found an opener, at least I think I have, but I'll leave you to work out how to use it. I'm rather fond of my fingers and don't fancy losing any of them!'

As she reached the bottom of the stairs she glanced up at the tall figure leaning on the banister rail. A ray of light from the narrow hall window added a burnished glow to her auburn hair, so that for a moment it seemed to be filled with an incandescent fire and flared against the muted drabness of her surroundings.

'What happened to all those liberated ideas of "anything you can do, I can do, too"?' he asked with a grin.

Mounting the stairs, Harriet paused to shake the dirty water from her feet and legs, idly noting the tide mark which skimmed just below the level of her shapely knees before briskly deciding to ignore it. There were more important things to worry about than a bit of dirt, namely some food for her rumbling stomach; pulling the folds of the dress free, she settled them around her before starting back up the stairs as she replied to his teasing.

'As I've never felt in the least bit oppressed, I've never felt the need to be liberated either, so you can forget that theory.'

Reaching the landing, she brushed past him, her skin shivering as it came into brief contact with the warmth of his body, making her realise just how cold it had been down in the water.

'So you're not one of those bra-burning ladies I was always reading about a couple of years back?' he asked, with a mocking inflection to his voice as he turned and paced along behind her.

'Not so far, though I must admit I was tempted this morning when I saw that contraption you'd left for me,' she said tartly.

Stepping ahead of him, she walked into the room and headed straight to the small stove, holding her hands out to the thin blue flames to try and warm them.

'Yes, well, it was probably a poor choice, I'll admit it. In fact, after further consideration, I'd say it's extremely doubtful if you'd need such an item at all.'

Slowly his eyes ran over her slender, shapely figure in the soft cotton dress, and Harriet felt all the heat she'd lost flood back in a sudden scalding tide. She turned away to hide her flushed face from his all too discerning vision. She'd had her share of boyfriends over the years and had learned to play the game of sexual banter with a fair degree of sophistication, but somehow whenever Rick passed even the tiniest comment it immediately threw her into a state of utter confusion, as though she was a young girl straight from a convent. Quite frankly, she couldn't understand it.

'Is that water ready yet?'

The pure practicality of the question steadied her, and after checking the bubbling water she nodded briefly.

'Yes. I'll make us some tea; we can have that first then heat up a tin of the soup later. I'm starving.'

Moving quickly and deftly, she made tea in an old metal pot, then poured it into two thick ring-striped mugs, leaving Rick's black as he requested and adding a small teaspoon of condensed milk to hers to colour it. Cradling the mug in her hands, she took a sip, shuddering at the unaccustomed sweetness, but grateful for the feeling of warmth it gave her. There was something so comforting about hot tea, no matter what the situation.

There was silence in the room as they drank, a strangely companionable silence she would never have believed possible between them; she glanced up under the thick veil of her dark lashes and let her eyes skim over the man seated opposite. How long had she known him? A week, but, measured in hours, only a bare fraction of that time, and yet here they were marooned in an empty house, sharing tea as though they'd known each other for years. He disturbed her, flicked feelings to life she'd never known she possessed, yet at the same time made her feel strangely comfortable with him. It was as though her body, her instincts recognised him, while her mind, that logical thinking part of her, maintained he was still a stranger. After all, just what did she know about him, apart from the fact that he was Mike's uncle and an actor? Just who was this man called Rick Dawson? Suddenly she was swamped by an insatiable urge to learn more about this tall, disturbing stranger.

'Whereabouts do you live, Rick?' she asked quietly, raising her head so that she could study him openly. For the briefest moment an expression of something akin to unease crossed his dark-tanned face, then it was gone so quickly that Harriet thought she must have imagined it. When he spoke, however, she was filled with a deep-seated conviction she'd been right in the first place, that he was reluctant to answer questions. Oh, his voice was low, easy, rock-steady in its measured tones, but instinct told her he was choosing his words with a singular amount of care, out of all proportion to the question. What was it he didn't want to tell her, didn't want her to know? There was something, she was sure of it. Sipping her tea, she watched him closely as he leant back in the chair, the mug of tea held loosely in one long-fingered lean hand.

'While I'm over here, I'm staying with my sister, Cathy, that's Mike's mother, and her husband Glen. Have you met them?'

'No, not yet. I've heard Jill speak about them several times, but I think she said they'd only been over here about two or three months.'

'It's nearer four now, though seeing as Glen's contract is for a minimum of two years you're bound to run into them sooner or later.'

'Oh, yes, in fact Jill was trying to arrange for us to meet before she went on holiday, but unfortunately there didn't seem to be enough time to fit it in.'

'Well, I'm sure you'll like them both, especially Cathy. She's a couple of years older than me and tries to mother me if I give her half a chance, but she's a lovely person, very warm and caring; everyone likes her.'

It was obvious from his tone that he was fond of his sister, and Harriet smiled, pleased to find they shared that bond. Then, still determined to find out more about him, she prompted gently, 'And home... where's that?'

'Santa Barbara,' he answered shortly.

'I've read about it. It's supposed to be a lovely place,' she said, her voice deliberately calm and encouraging. Slowly she ran her eyes over his face, but he seemed to have slipped a bland mask into place at the mention of his home town, which betrayed absolutely nothing of what he was thinking. Obviously if she wanted to learn more about him then she would have to draw him out, let the conversation ebb and flow naturally, then see how much he revealed. Although he might appear easy and open on the surface, that light mockery was really a cover for feelings and emotions which ran far deeper. To put it bluntly, Rick Dawson was a smiling, charming mystery, one she intended to solve!

'Yes, it is, very lovely. One of the most beautiful coastlines I've ever seen.'

'And do you live on your own, or have you any other family, apart from Cathy, that is?'

He hesitated, the tiniest of brief pauses which Harriet mightn't have noticed if she hadn't been watching him so closely.

'Yes, I live on my own. I've a house on the coast,' he answered, standing to set his drained mug back on the small table so that his back was towards her. 'How about you?'

'Me? Oh, I live on my own too, apart from Caspar, that is,' she replied readily, eager to keep the conversational ball rolling.

'And who's looking after him while you're away?' he asked, turning to rest a lean hip against the wood.

'Ken...that's my next-door neighbour. He always keeps an eye on him for me if I have to go away, and in return I keep an eye on his taxi...the one I was driving that day I met you,' she said with a grin.

'I see, so I've really got Ken to thank for at least one comfortable journey,' he said wryly. 'What were you doing at the airport in it, though? I never did find out.'

'Oh, I'd offered to give my sister Jill and her husband a lift so they could catch their plane. They won a holiday to the Bahamas in a breakfast cereal competition, the first thing Jill's ever won after heaven knows how many years of entering competitions, but the problem was Betsy wouldn't start that morning so I borrowed the cab to get them there, seeing as Ken was away.'

'And he didn't mind?'

'Well, he wasn't too happy about it when I told him, but as everything was still in one piece he couldn't really shout, just made me promise not to do it again unless it was a matter of life or death!' Harriet admitted with a soft laugh. 'Still, at least it got them to the airport on time; I'd never have forgiven myself if they'd missed their flight, not after all I'd gone through to make Jill accept the prize.'

'I wouldn't have thought anyone would be reluctant to accept a free holiday,' he said with an astonished glance in Harriet's direction, and she grimaced.

'It wasn't really that she was reluctant, but she'd already promised to take the cubs on camp, and Dave had booked his holidays so he could go with them. Unfortunately, there was no way he could change his weeks so they could have the holiday later. It was a case of either then or never, and Jill just wasn't prepared to go back on her promise and let people down. It took me ages to persuade her to let me fill in for her on camp.'

'So that's how you came to be going; I had wondered.'

'Yes, not that it looks like I'm going to be much help at the moment, does it? I only hope they've fared better than we have so far. You don't think they'll have been caught in the flood, do you, Rick?'

A sudden fear reared up inside her at the thought of Danny and the rest of the boys being caught in the middle of the flood, and she raised her eyes to his, mutely asking for reassurance.

'No, I don't think they'll be in any danger at all, so don't start worrying about them. When Pat was telling me about the campsite, I remember her saying it was on fairly high ground, cut into a hillside, if I'm not mistaken, so I doubt if they'll have even seen the flood, let alone have been caught in it. I'd hazard a guess that we're the only ones out of the group who are stranded.'

'Well, thank heavens for that, though Pat's probably going frantic wondering where we've got to.'

'I'm sure she'll realise what's happened. There are bound to have been flood warnings on the radio, and after all it will probably only be for a couple of days at the most. Tell you what, if I open that tin of soup you mentioned, how about making us some lunch while I go out and check the level of the water? Then we can get some idea of when we'll be able to get away from here.'

'Yes, all right. I suppose it's really all we can do for the moment,' she agreed with a small, worried frown.

It was only later, with the soup simmering in the pan, that Harriet realised what he'd done. She picked up the old metal spoon and stirred the hot liquid with an unwarranted vigour. He'd done it so neatly, so easily, turning the questions aside so that she knew no more

about him now than she'd done half an hour earlier.
While she'd thought she was drawing him out, he'd very
neatly turned the tables on her! If she wanted to know
more about Rick Dawson, then it was obvious it would
need more than a few delicately framed questions to find
it . . . more like a full-scale mining operation!

CHAPTER SEVEN

THE LIGHT was fading, too dim now for her to see properly, yet not quite dark enough to warrant lighting the lamps and burning any of their precious supply of oil. With a sigh Harriet folded the cover over the tablet of creamy paper, and pulled open the shallow drawer of the table to slide it inside, her eyes sweeping over the small collection of pencils and charcoals she'd found earlier with a feeling of familiar contentment. Somehow it was comforting to know that someone who'd lived in the house had shared this desire to draw with her; in some indefinable way it made her feel less like an intruder.

Closing the drawer carefully on the little hoard, she stood up and crossed the room to stare unseeingly out of the window at the flat, leaden sea of water, her hands rubbing over the goose-bumps on her bare arms in an effort to warm them into submission. The whole of the house felt damp, not surprising really with about two feet of water swilling round downstairs, and now that night was drawing in it had turned rather cold. Perhaps she should go back to the room she'd used and find a sweater before she ended up with a chill.

Glad of something positive to do, Harriet hurried from the room along the darkening landing, pausing as she came level with the door to the room Rick was using. It was so quiet, so very silent, except for the faint whisper of sound from the water moving downstairs, that it made her edgy, filled her with a sudden childish urge to sing or shout, do anything to break the oppressive silence. What was Rick doing in there? Surely he couldn't still be sleeping, could he? He'd gone to his room several hours back, pleading a tiredness evident from the pallor which lay under his tanned skin, but surely he should be awake by now?

Suddenly inexplicably worried, Harriet tapped lightly on the door, her ear pressed to the cold, damp wood as she waited for an answer, but there was nothing, nothing but the soft swishing sound of water echoing up the stairs, and she shuddered, turning quickly away. Walking rapidly along the rest of the passage, she hurried into her room and, closing the door, leant back against it, her heart hammering in a fast little rhythm. She felt tense, on edge, but she just didn't know why. After all, it wasn't as if she was unused to being on her own, but there was just something about the whispering quietness of the house which was making her nervous.

Chiding herself for being so foolish, she pushed away from the door and pulled open the drawers of the dresser to find a sweater. The choice was abysmal, but finally she settled on a worn-thin purple cardigan which did little if anything for her vivid colouring, but at least looked as if it would fit her. Pulling it on, she buttoned it quickly up to her throat, feeling the faint shudder which raced through her body at the sudden welcome warmth of an extra layer. She smiled wryly. The only thing really wrong with her at the moment was that she was both cold and bored. Well, she'd done something about the cold, so maybe she should do something about the boredom and wake Rick up. After all, there was no way she could ever call that man boring!

Within seconds she was back outside his room; she stepped softly inside, her eyes shooting straight to the bed where he was still sleeping. On quiet feet she crossed the bare wooden plank floor and stared down at him, feeling the faint, unsettling quiver which raced through her as she studied his face. With the lids covering those jewel-coloured eyes and the firm, tough lines of his face relaxed by sleep, he looked strangely young, strangely vulnerable, and in a sudden flash Harriet knew she was seeing yet another side to Rick Dawson, another one to add to the many she'd seen already. First there'd been the rough, tough gangster who'd pushed her around, determined she wasn't going to get the better of him, then there'd been the easy, charming stranger who'd calmly stated he intended to make her like him, then the hero who'd jumped into the river to save her with absolutely no regard for his own safety and finally, just hours earlier, the man of mystery who'd so determinedly guarded his secrets. So many people, or rather so many sides to just one person, but which one of them was the real Rick Dawson? If she only knew that, then maybe she'd have some idea how to handle him!

He turned, the movement so sudden that it startled her, and she jumped, pressing a hand to her throat to still the frantic pulse-beat. Meeting his gaze, she smiled shakily at him and felt an icy finger of panic trace down her spine when he failed to respond but just stared blankly back at her.

'Rick! Rick, are you all right?'

She brought her face closer to his, wondering if he could see her properly in the dim light, and she felt her heart lurch with relief as he answered slowly.

'Yes, I think so...I was having a dream, I think. I don't know—it all seems kind of hazy now.'

Sitting up, he rubbed his hands over his face, a sharp hissing gasp of pain leaving his lips as he stretched the wound on his side.

'Is that cut bothering you?'

Sitting down on the edge of the bed, Harriet studied him closely, noting the flush which now stained his lean cheeks, replacing the recent veil of pallor. Heat was coming from his body in waves, yet now she was so close she could see he was shivering, could even feel the faint quiver which made his body tremble in an insistent rhythm, and that icy finger spread to a handspan of fear. From the look of things he was running a fever, and she sent up a silent little prayer that it wasn't the wound on his side that was causing it. Forcing a calmness to her voice she was far from feeling, she said firmly, 'Just let me take a look at your side, Rick, while I check the dressing.'

She unbuttoned the thick plaid shirt he was wearing and eased it free from his trousers to expose the make-shift bandage.

'Doesn't seem right, somehow: a beautiful woman starts undressing me and I'm unable to take her up on it!'

There was a lightness to his tone which didn't fool Harriet for a moment. He was in pain, a good deal of it from the look of things, but she knew he'd never actually admit it. She carefully unwound the bandage, murmuring an apology as she heard him catch his breath as she worked it free from his skin to examine the gash. It still looked sore and painful, but no worse, thankfully, than it had done in the morning, and she felt the tight knot of fear ease just a fraction.

'Well, Nurse, do you think I'll make it?'

The low, teasing voice seemed easier now, less forced, and immediately Harriet responded to it.

'I'm quite sure you'll be fine, Mr Dawson, if you just follow orders. Now keep still while I rewind this bandage.'

Rolling the strip of cloth, she rebound the pad into place, her fingers more deft than they'd been earlier.

'This is something I could learn to enjoy after a while,' he said softly and Harriet looked up, a sparky reply forming on her lips, a reply which fizzled out like a damp squib when her mouth brushed unexpectedly against his.

There was a moment's stillness, as though the whole world had been set on hold, then slowly Rick moved, easing his mouth more firmly down on to hers and kissing her with a devastating, heart-stopping thoroughness. For a second, just for that tiniest of moments, she responded, before pulling back and trying to set some distance between them, suddenly terrified of all the sensations which had sprung to life at the feel of his lips and threatened to take hold of her reason.

'Rick, you mustn't! You're not well. This is...'

'Oh, it is, Harriet, it most definitely is!'

Gently, firmly, he pulled her back, his long hands curving round the back of her head, his fingers burrowing through the soft, rich curls to rub over the delicate bones of her skull in a caress which made her burn with a liquid fire. Then, moving with a dreamlike softness, he whispered kisses along the curve of her brow, down the soft slope of her cheek to the very corner of her mouth and stopped.

'Kiss me, Harriet,' he murmured, his voice deep and soft, and Harriet knew she was powerless to resist the gentle command. She met his lips with a sudden urgency, needing to taste his kiss, to feel the clean, firm line of his lips against hers, to feel the fire run through her again. The kiss flared, fuelled by an overwhelming blaze of passion. He kissed her and she kissed him back, wanting to give him as much pleasure as he gave her, wanting to sear her brand on his lips, as he did on hers. Then slowly they drew apart and there was silence, a silence which echoed with a thousand unspoken words and feelings; a silence she didn't want him to break with explanations and questions she couldn't answer.

'Harriet, I...'

'I...I think I'd better make us a drink, Rick. Come through when you're ready. Don't rush.'

She was gabbling, she knew it, the words tossing and tumbling from her lips like a frothy flow of water, but she couldn't help it. All she knew was that she had to get away, had to have a few seconds by herself while she regathered her scattered senses.

She fled from the room, her legs weak, her whole body trembling in reaction, her breath panting in spurts, as though she'd just run a race. Hurrying along the dark landing to the room where they'd set up the stove, she poured water from a bucket into the old pan and set it on the burner, her hands shaking as she held a match out to light it.

It had just been a kiss, after all, just a brief exchange between a man and a woman, quite natural in the circumstances, so why did she feel so utterly shaken, as though she'd just reached the very edge of a precipice and suddenly tumbled over?

'It's pointless to run away, Harriet. You can't change anything by doing that.'

The low voice came from the doorway, and desperately she schooled her face into blankness before shooting a brief look over her shoulder.

'I really don't know what you're talking about. Now, what do you want to drink...tea, or some of that Bovril?'

Moving away from the stove, she sorted quickly through the small collection of groceries stashed on a gate-legged table, cursing softly as she knocked the can of condensed milk over. Creamy thick milk poured from the can, and she looked round for a cloth, her heart leaping painfully as Rick came up alongside her.

'Here.'

For a second she stared blankly down at the piece of old cloth in his hands before silently taking it from him and mopping up the mess. Her fingers were sticky, filmed with milk, and she scooped up a small measure of water into an old enamel bowl to rinse them, glad of an excuse not to face him just at that moment. There was no way she wanted him to know just how much that kiss had affected her, no way at all. Instinct told her it would be playing with fire. She had to remember the fact that they were here alone in the house and that it would be all too easy to let herself be caught up by feelings she might possibly regret later. She had to be sensible. Taking a deep, steadying breath, she turned, her face calm as she stared at him across the narrow width of the table.

'Listen, Rick, there's one thing we have to get clear, here and now. We've got to live together for the next few days, and there's no way we can do that if we let things get out of hand. It's only natural that we might— well, might start to feel a certain attraction for each other, but we can't follow through on it.'

'No?'

He drew out a chair and sat down, his eyes never leaving her face, so that she could feel the colour start to steal once more under her skin. But there was no way he was going to sway her from what she'd decided, from what she knew was right. Rick Dawson was a potent mixture of masculine charm and sheer sensuality, but she was going to resist him...now, while she was still able. She had the feeling it could be far more difficult later!

'No, Rick. Look, I'm attracted to you, I'll admit it, but that's as far as it goes and not a step further. There's no way I'm going to end up in bed with you, so let's get that straight.'

She set two mugs on to the table with a firm little clatter which somehow boosted up her sagging courage. She was right to spell it all out to him, to state quite clearly her views on their relationship, and the knowledge was quietly comforting.

'OK, so you've admitted you're attracted to me—well, if we're being honest, then I have to say that I'm attracted to you, more than just attracted, in fact, but frankly I think you're deluding yourself,' Rick pointed out.

'Deluding myself...what do you mean?' Harriet stared at him, a puzzled frown creasing the smooth skin of her brow.

'I mean that emotions are unpredictable, and there's no way you can state categorically that you're not going to get more involved with me than you are now. It just doesn't work like that, as you should know.'

The comfort was dripping away now, like honey off the end of a warm spoon, and Harriet looked away, frightened he might see her mounting fear and act on it while she was still so very vulnerable. She had to be calm, rational, convince him of her determination.

'I'm afraid I just don't agree with you.'

'No? Well, think back to yesterday, to that statement you made in the car on the way here.'

'Statement ... what statement?'

Flicking off the burner, Harriet took her time wrapping a towel round the handle of the old pan before she lifted it to pour water on to the tea in the pot, her face still averted.

'Now, how did it go exactly? I know—you said you wouldn't like me if I was the last man on earth. Be honest, Harriet, how do you feel about me now? Can you really and truly say that you haven't changed your mind, that you still don't like me?'

The question hung in the air, spanning the silence which had fallen between them, and Harriet felt her heart start to pound as she tried to frame an answer. She met his gaze, her eyes dark in the paleness of her face, and with a sudden jolt knew she couldn't lie to him.

'No, Rick,' she said softly. 'No, I can't say that at all.'

And she saw the brief triumph which crossed his face, with a tiny gnawing ache of fear.

'*Ziggurat!* There's no way you can have that, Rick. You're cheating!'

Tossing the handful of lettered squares down on to the table, Harriet sat back, folding her arms as she stared stormily at the man seated opposite, her lips set in a mutinous line.

'Cheating? Me, cheating? I ask you, honey, would I do such a thing? No, "ziggurat" is a word, but if you don't believe me then go downstairs and find a dictionary to check it out. I remember seeing some books in one of the rooms last night, so there's bound to be one there.'

He smiled at her as he leant back in his chair, a teasing curve to his lips as he noticed her expressive shudder, and she glared stormily back at him. There was no way she was going downstairs to wade through all that water in the pitch darkness, and he knew it! He could have his points and she hoped they choked him!

Picking up the stub of pencil, Harriet added the score to Rick's total, wincing as she saw just how many points the word had given him. They'd been playing Scrabble for over an hour now, and though Harriet had always considered herself fairly good at the game it had quickly become obvious that he, too, was no novice. When Rick had first found the game in the back of a cupboard it had seemed the perfect and most innocuous way of passing the evening, giving neither of them time to think of anything other than the swift arrangement of letters on the board. Now, however, she wasn't so certain; there was no way she wanted him to beat her!

Swiftly she ran the tip of the pencil down the long line of figures, totting up the scores, then tossed it aside with a small murmur of disgust as she realised he'd won by more than sixteen clear points.

'I take it I'm the winner, then?' he asked with a mock innocence, and she nodded.

'Yes, seems like it, though I'm sure some of those words owed more to your imagination than any dictionary!'

He laughed, the low sound echoing round the small room, and unwillingly Harriet smiled too, unable to resist the warm sound.

'Well, I have to admit that some, only some, mind you, mightn't have been quite right, but it wasn't intentional.'

'Oh, no? Well, if you think I'll believe that, then you can think again. You, Rick Dawson, set out to win, and from the look of things you weren't too bothered about how you did it.'

Scooping the lettered wooden squares into a pile, Harriet slid them back into the box and closed the lid, her fingers rubbing across its dusty surface.

'What's the point in playing if you don't go all out to win, Harriet? No, one thing you should know about me is that I always play to win.'

And Harriet knew with a sudden insight that he was no longer talking about boardgames. Looking up, she let her eyes trace over his face, and shivered as she saw the determination etched in its lines. Once before he'd said he enjoyed a challenge, and now she knew he hadn't been joking. Beneath all that easy, laid-back charm lay a steely character. Rick Dawson would always play to win!

'Well, as it looks as if you're not going to give me another game, we may as well call it a night. Despite all that sleep I had earlier, I'm still tired. It must be this country air.'

He pushed back the chair, stretched the cramped muscles in his back and winced.

'God, this side is painful! Next time you go falling into a river, Harriet, try to make certain it's not full of logs, will you? I don't enjoy being ground to a pulp.'

His eyes were softly teasing and Harriet smiled back at him, the sudden surge of worry forgotten in the warmth of his look.

'Well, I didn't really choose to fall in, as you well know, but just for you, Rick, next time I'll be more careful to find a better place.'

Moving round the end of the table, she turned out one of the oil lamps then picked up the other to light their way along the dark landing. Stopping outside Rick's room, she waited while he turned the handle and opened the door, her eyes studying his profile. Although he'd seemed well enough while they'd been playing, she'd noticed him shivering several times, as though his body couldn't derive enough warmth from the thick shirt and sweater he was wearing, and it worried her. Perhaps he'd caught a chill from yesterday's soaking in the storm, or when he'd dived into the river to save her. A sudden huge wave of guilt rose up and swamped her. If he was ill, then it was her fault and she had to face it.

'And what are you looking so serious about now?'

The low question made her jump and she hesitated, trying to find some way of telling him just how sorry she was for all the upset she'd caused him, but it wasn't easy. There was no way she wanted to talk herself into the sort of apology he'd asked for earlier!

'I was—well, I was just feeling guilty,' she mumbled finally.

'Guilty? What on earth for? Don't tell me you were cheating at Scrabble, too, Miss Prince,' he said in mock anger.

'No, of course I wasn't,' she retorted sharply. 'There wasn't enough space on the board for two of us to cheat in! No, what I'm feeling guilty about is all the bother I've given you, running out of petrol, getting lost, having you jump in the river after me. I seem to have caused you nothing but trouble since we set out on that journey, and I suppose I want you to know just how much I regret it.'

'Do you? I don't.'

'You don't? What on earth do you mean? No one could have enjoyed all the hassle you've been through these past few hours.' Moving the lamp aside, she stared at him in astonishment, wondering if he was sicker than she'd realised, and he chuckled.

'Well, maybe I could have lived quite happily without *all* those incidents you mentioned,' he said wryly, a mocking tilt to his long mouth, 'but frankly, there's no way I would have missed a minute of your company. You, Harriet Prince, are a fascinating lady, dangerous to be around, admittedly, but most definitely fascinating.'

He pressed a soft kiss to the side of her mouth, his eyes deeply green in the gentle glow from the lamp as he stared down at her. 'Goodnight, Harriet. Sweet dreams!'

He stepped inside the room, closing the door softly behind him, leaving her staring after him, speechless from what could only be described as pleasure. Damn him!

It was difficult to know just what had wakened her, for when finally she forced her sleepy eyes open there was nothing but silence, a deep, thick silence unscarred by any lingering echo of sound. Lying in bed, Harriet let her eyes adjust slowly to the darkness then looked round, searching for anything in the shadows which could have disturbed her, but there was nothing, nothing but the faint silvered glow from a cloud-patched moon striking off dusty surfaces. With a sigh she turned over, pulling the blankets closer round her shoulders.

It was so cold, cold and damp with an edge to the chill which penetrated through to her bones. She shivered, huddling deeper into the covers. Closing her eyes, she willed herself back to sleep, forcing herself to breathe slowly and deeply in a steady rhythm, but it was useless. Sleep had gone and she was wide awake.

Turning on to her back, she gazed at the patterns of light and shadow on the cracked ceiling, her mind suddenly unbearably busy with a thousand thoughts she'd rather not face up to. What was that saying about the darkest hour before the dawn? Well, she mightn't have a watch to tell her the time, but instinct told her she'd just hit it to the second. Suddenly all the emotions, all the feelings she'd held in check through the long, disturbing day rose up to swamp her, and she was filled by an unquenchable fear.

Had Rick been right when he'd said emotions couldn't be controlled, couldn't be turned on and off at will? She just didn't know. She'd never had any difficulty in controlling her emotions before, but somehow, ever since she'd first met him, things seemed to have changed, so that now she was suddenly less certain of her own ability. She had to face the one undeniable fact that just over twenty-four hours ago she'd believed herself incapable of liking Rick Dawson, and yet look how all that had changed. Would she, in another twenty-four hours' time, still be able to stick to the decision she'd made, or would that have changed, too? That was what really frightened her.

She was attracted to Rick far more than she'd ever been to any other man before. When he touched her she burned, and there was just no other way to describe it; she burned with a savage, all-consuming fire which owed little to reason. He was a stranger to her, yet her body responded to him as though it had known his touch for years. It didn't seem to matter that deep down she sensed there was something he was keeping from her; all she knew was that when he kissed her the whole world narrowed down to that moment. So was it only liking she felt for him, liking plus attraction and gratitude for the way he'd saved her, or was it something more, some far deeper emotion? Could this rage of feeling that rose up inside her be the beginnings of love?

She rolled over and pushed her face into the pillow, trying to force the idea from her mind just as she forced the dim light from her vision, but it refused to go, refused to be snuffed out like a mere candle, and she moaned aloud in a sudden, sharp anguish. She couldn't be in love with him, she couldn't!

A faint sound echoed through the house, cutting into her thoughts to send her heart leaping in a sudden primeval fear, and she sat up, clutching the blankets round her. It came again, a soft, uneven shuffling from the landing. Holding her breath, Harriet strained to identify it, a small nervous laugh escaping from her lips as she realised it was footsteps. Rick must have been to the bathroom, and that was what had disturbed her earlier.

Leaning back against the pillows, she closed her eyes, feeling the rapid beat of her heart slow into a more even rhythm, feeling the panic start to ease from her mind. She'd been foolish to allow such fanciful thoughts to upset her, foolish and very silly. All she felt for Rick was pure sexual attraction, nothing more and definitely nothing as earth-shattering as love! Granted, nothing like it had ever happened to her before, but that was probably why it had come as such a shock to her system, throwing her completely off balance. She'd always believed herself too level-headed and rational to be caught up by the chemistry of sexual attraction, but now she knew better! She was just as susceptible as anyone when the right person came along, and the only strange thing was that person should be Rick Dawson. But it definitely wasn't love!

Reassured, she burrowed once more beneath the blankets, but after ten long sleepless minutes knew it was useless. Sleep had been wrenched from her mind, torn aside by her foolish fancies, and there was no way it would return for what was left of the night. She tossed back the covers and climbed wearily out of bed, thrusting her arms into the hideous purple cardi and shivering violently as the icy cold seeped into her thinly clad body. She might as well make a drink, then draw until dawn finally broke; at least that would keep her mind busy.

She walked quietly along the landing, tiptoeing past the part-open door to Rick's bedroom so she wouldn't wake him.

'Harriet.'

The low, husky voice stopped her, and she pushed the door wider open.

'Yes? Sorry if I disturbed you, I was just going for a drink. I couldn't sleep.'

Stepping into the room, she peered through the gloom, her eyes widening in surprise as she saw he was lying on top of the blankets, his body bare to the waist. Surely he couldn't be that hot, could he? It was as icy cold in his room as it had been in hers.

'Do you think you could fetch me a drink, too? I'm parched.'

There was a dry, cracked note to his deep voice that immediately alarmed her, and she moved closer and stared down at him in concern, quickly noting the perspiration beaded across his forehead. She laid the back of her hand against his cheek, and almost pulled back in alarm as she felt the heat of his skin.

'How long have you been burning up like this, Rick?' she asked quickly.

'Oh, an hour, maybe longer. I don't know.'

'An hour?'

It was a long time, too long in her estimation, but there was no way she wanted to alarm him. Forcing a lightness to her voice, she said calmly, 'Well, you just lie still while I go and get you that drink, and maybe a damp cloth to sponge you with. We must try and get that temperature down before you boil!'

With a faint smile she turned and hurried from the room along the landing, stumbling slightly as her foot caught painfully against the leg of a chair just inside the doorway to their makeshift kitchen. Arms outstretched to feel for any other obstacles, she made her way slowly across the room to the small table and hunted round for the matches to light the lamp. Snatching up the small box, she pushed it open, matches scattering across the bare floor in a shower as her hands started to shake in a sudden fit of nerves.

Suppose Rick was really ill; what could she do? What did she know about caring for a sick person? Her first-aid certificate might be adequate for cuts and bruises, but it was hardly the best qualification to deal with a real illness, was it? Fast and furious the questions flew through her mind as she tried to light the lamp, but when eventually a soft pale glow illuminated the drab room, she was still no closer to finding the answers. Of course, she'd do the best she could for him, but if it wasn't enough and he needed proper medical attention, then the only course open to her would be to go for help, and that wasn't going to be as easy as it sounded. Although the flood water was draining away, it was still deep enough to cover the fields and roads, making travelling any distance almost impossible. Then, even supposing she could wade through the water, she'd still have another problem to contend with, namely which way to go. She had absolutely no idea where they were at present, nor in which direction she should turn to find the help he needed; she might have to travel for miles before she came upon any place suitable. It was a frighteningly grim realisation.

Sighing, she forced her thoughts away from all the things which might happen and back to what she had to contend with at the moment; and her first priority must be to get Rick's temperature down somehow. It was dangerously high and there was no way she could leave him in that state much longer. Although there was obviously nothing in the way of medication she could give him, she could at least, as she'd suggested, sponge him down and try to make him that bit more comfortable. She scooped water from the bucket into the enamel bowl, then set it aside on the table while she filled a mug with some of the cool boiled water left in the pan. There was no way she could take a chance on letting him drink water straight from the tap at the moment while he was so vulnerable, in case it had been contaminated during the flood. The last thing that poor man needed was tainted water!

Working quickly, she arranged the items on a small wooden tray and carefully balanced it in one hand while she lifted the lamp with the other to light her way. Behind the night-darkened surface of the uncurtained window she could see the first pale streaks of dawn breaking, but it would be an hour or more before the light was strong enough to see by. Taking a deep, steadying breath, she walked purposefully along the landing, trying desperately to ignore the heavy, painful pounding of her nervous heart. She'd cope, she'd have to...after all, there was no one else.

Rick was lying as she'd left him, eyes closed, his breath coming in a heavy, rasping gasp which alarmed her almost more than the heat of his skin had done earlier. Moving closer, she held the lamp up and studied him, her eyes tracing over the deep colour which rimmed his hard cheekbones with fire. His eyes flickered open, their green depths dull and hazy with fever, and he stared up at her for a long, heart-stopping moment, then he smiled, the barest movement of his parched, cracked lips, which must have cost him a vast amount of effort.

'The lady with the lamp. Nurse Florence, I presume.'

That he could try and make light of it all for her sake, when she knew he felt so ill, moved her so that she suddenly found herself unable to speak as tears welled up to choke her.

'Oh, sweetheart, don't cry! I'm not dead yet,' he said softly, his voice teasing. Reaching out, he brushed her hand with his, his skin burning against the coldness of her fingers. 'It'll be all right, Harriet, believe me.'

'Will it? Oh, Rick, I'm so frightened; I don't know what to do for you.'

'Shh. It'll be all right, you'll see,' he repeated, his fingers pressing hers for a moment before dropping away. 'Now, how about that drink you promised me?'

Levering himself awkwardly up against the wooden headboard, he met her eyes, his gaze steady and somehow reassuring, and with a slight nod Harriet followed his bidding. Setting the tray and lamp on the small bedside-table, she sat down on the edge of the bed and handed him the cup, watching as he sipped slowly at the cool water till it was all finished. Taking the empty cup from him, she put it aside, then wrung a cloth out in the bowl of water and slowly, methodically, wiped it over his face and down the strong column of his neck, feeling him shiver.

'That feels good,' he murmured.

'Does it? Well, I've always wanted to soothe a fevered brow,' she replied, trying to match his mood with a determined levity. 'Now, why don't you lie down while I sponge you a bit more and see if we can get that temperature down.'

Putting an arm round his shoulders, she helped him lie down on the bed, noting the way he favoured his sore side as though frightened of taking any pressure on it. Damping the cloth again in the water, she stroked it gently over his heated skin, sponging over the perspiration-soaked muscles of his chest and arms as well as his face. His breathing was still heavy and rasping, but he seemed a little easier, as though the reduction in heat was lessening his discomfort. Gradually he slipped into an uneasy doze, but Harriet continued with her gentle bathing till her hand and arm ached with the continuous movement, her eyes never leaving his face. He had to get better, he just had to! As she looked down at him, this suddenly seemed the most important thing she'd ever wished for in the whole of her life.

Dawn broke slowly, gently, sending a rosy, sweet light over the countryside and in through the uncurtained windows, but Harriet barely noticed its arrival. Rick's condition had changed in the past half-hour, the burning fever turning to racking spasms of shivering when his body shook with a startling violence as it tried to generate some heat. She'd covered him as best she could with the blankets, had even been and stripped the clothes from her own bed to add to his, but nothing seemed to be enough to warm him. Staring down at his shuddering form, Harriet felt herself grow tense with fear and anguish at her own inability to help him.

If only there was some way of heating the room, then maybe she could make him more comfortable, but one swift glance around the bare room soon convinced her it was impossible. The fireplace had been boarded up and plastered over, and even if she managed to open it up again there was no knowing what state the chimney might be in or how it would react to a fire. It was hopeless. Staring down at him, Harriet desperately tried to think of some way to bring warmth back to his cold-tortured body, and suddenly it came to her, sweet and simple. There was only one way of warming him, the only way, as far as she could see, and that was with a hot-water bottle . . . a human one . . . her.

For a split second she hesitated, her mind balking at such an intimacy, but the sight of the sudden violent spasm which racked him was all she needed. Shrugging off the skirt and sweater she'd pulled on over her night-shirt, she slid into bed next to him and gathered him close, feeling the way his body shook and trembled against hers.

'Harriet?'

Colour flared gently into her cheeks as his eyes opened and stared into hers, but she refused to be embarrassed by her actions. He was ill, and if this was the only way of helping him, then so be it. Running the palm of her hand gently down his cheek, she pressed his head tighter into the hollow of her shoulder, her voice soft and soothing as she whispered gently, 'It's all right, Rick, lie still. I'm just going to warm you, that's all.'

He stared at her, green eyes heavy and hazy, then his lips curved into a slow smile and Harriet felt something catch inside her as she saw it. Slowly his lids drifted down and he slept, a deep, healing sleep, and after a while his body no longer shook but drew warmth from hers and lay heavy and relaxed against her. Looking at him, filled almost to the brim with that surge of tenderness that had swept through her, Harriet knew she would hold this time in her heart for ever.

CHAPTER EIGHT

HE SLEPT for over an hour, and all that time Harriet held him, ignoring the stiffness which ached through her arms and shoulder from the pressure of his body. Daylight came fully, a bright golden sun lighting the heavy skies, pouring warmth in through the window, but still she refused to relinquish her burden. She'd been so frightened, so terrified of what might happen to him, that she no longer cared what he might think when he woke and found her next to him. All she knew was that nothing had ever felt so good, so right as the weight of his sleeping body resting against her.

Staring down at him, her eyes tracing over the golden stubble which roughened his chin, the faint, fine lines fanned around his closed eyes, there was no longer any way she could fool herself into believing that all she felt for this man was physical attraction. It was more than that, far, far more, though whether it went as far as love was something she wasn't yet prepared to decide on. All that mattered was that she was there, holding him, caring for him; everything else was unimportant.

He stirred, his body moving briefly against hers, before slowly his eyes slid open and he stared straight up at her.

'Good morning,' she said, a gentle smile curving her lips. 'How do you feel?'

'Better, much better... I think.'

'Only think?' she queried, a slight frown puckering her brow.

128

'Mmm. I think I'm better, but maybe I'm not, maybe I'm still feverish and hallucinating, otherwise how else can I explain finding you here in my bed, the one place you swore you'd never be?'

He was teasing her, but she still coloured, the delicate pink sweeping under her fair skin in a rosy tide as she answered stiffly, 'You were sick, and it was the only way I could think of to help you.'

'Was it? Well, all I can say is I should be sick more often if this is the treatment for it.'

Raising his head, he feathered his lips softly over the curve of hers, and Harriet felt a sudden surge of feeling well up inside her. Reason told her she should get up, get out of this bed and his arms now, while she was still able, but somehow she couldn't find the strength or the will to do so while his lips worked their magic on her.

His hand traced gently over the silken skin of her arm in a caress which sent fire racing through her veins, and she trembled, unable to hide her reaction at this light touch. Gently, his fingers moved up her arm along the delicate bones of her shoulder to push the neck of the shirt open and slide inside, and Harriet caught her breath as she desperately tried to regain some of her far-scattered senses. She tried to make some distance between them, but he refused to let her move more than an inch from his side.

'Rick, I must get up. It's late and...'

'Late? Late for what? Not for this, surely?'

Gently, firmly, he pulled her back, his eyes meeting hers for one long moment, an expression in them which Harriet couldn't put into words, but which made her shudder with an overpowering surge of longing, and suddenly she knew it was too late, at least for her. There was no way she wanted to leave him, to get out of the bed and listen to reason. All she wanted to do was follow her feelings and let them guide her along whichever path they chose. Lifting her hand, she stroked it down the softly rough curve of his cheek, her eyes dark as they stared into his.

There was a moment's stillness, when she had the strangest feeling he was wrestling with some inner decision, then it was gone, swept away by the undeniable surge of passion which flared between them. Holding her to him, he covered her face with a shower of burning kisses, and she moaned deep in her throat, pressing her body closer and closer against the hardness of his. Her heart was pounding, thumping in a heavy, breath-snatching rhythm matched by his, and a sudden fierce, sweet pleasure raced through her that she could make him want her as much as she wanted him. She met his lips, putting an end to the teasing, tormenting rainshower of kisses, and kissed him with a demanding passion. Then everything was touch, sensation, movement, pleasure, as he pressed her lips open and kissed her deeply, his tongue stroking round the softness of her mouth.

Flash-fire shot through her body and she pressed herself closer, needing to feel him so warm and alive against her, and in that way exorcise the very last of those haunting night-time fears from her mind. He was here, he was safe, and for now at least he was hers...

His arms locked round her, his body shuddering against the softness of hers, one hand lifting to stroke over the tumbled curls at the back of her head before moving slowly down the slim, smooth column of her throat to the neck of her shirt. With deft, gentle fingers he eased the tiny buttons open and slid his hand inside to cup the fullness of her breast, and Harriet gasped at this new and wonderful sensation he was creating. Arching against him in an untutored, instinctive response, she could feel her breasts swell at his touch, feel the nipples harden as he brushed his knuckles over them time after time in a slow, exquisite rhythm. A spiralling tide of warmth was starting low in her stomach, curling through her body, filling her till she was mindless of everything except his touch and her own undeniable hunger. She wanted him, so much...now.

Suddenly there was a noise, a heavy insistent pounding which filtered even through her passion-dimmed hearing, and she went rigid, listening. It came again, louder, longer, the sound echoing round and round the quiet house in a demanding rhythm; the sound of someone knocking!

'My God, I don't believe it!'

Rick rested his forehead against hers for a moment, his whole body trembling, shuddering in reaction, and she held him to her, fighting back the tears of frustration which had sprung to her eyes. Of all the times for anyone to come calling, why did it have to be now?

She watched dumbly as he flung back the blankets and dragged on the shirt and trousers he'd worn last night then strode from the room without a backward glance. She shivered, tiny, trembling spasms trickling through her body like icy wavelets as the cold reality of what had so nearly happened flooded in like a winter tide. For several minutes she lay unmoving in the rumpled bed as the enormity of it all filled her, and she knew there was no point in trying to fool herself into believing she would have stopped him. She'd wanted to make love with him, wanted it with a deep, burning longing which made a mockery of all her dearly held principles and convictions. For all these years she'd truly believed it was her own moral fibre which had made her resist temptation, but now she knew she'd been wrong. Temptation had just never come before in the right package!

He'd not forced her, not seduced her or coerced her; he'd not had to, she'd been a more than willing participant, equalling his passion with her own. Wave after wave of embarrassment rose up inside her as she remembered how she'd pressed herself against him, her body inviting his to the greatest intimacy of all, and she groaned, pushing her face into the pillow to muffle the sound. How could she ever face him again...how?

The thought galvanised her into action and she jumped up, legs trembling as she stood by the bed, pulling on the skirt and sweater. Then she quickly hurried from the room, half running along the landing to the head of the stairs and peering down into the hallway.

The water had fallen, a thick, muddy scum now all that was left to cover the wooden flooring and cling to the thigh-high boots of the two police officers standing by the open front door. Hearing her footsteps, they looked up, and Harriet forced a thin, tight smile to her lips as she greeted them.

'Good morning.'

Unbidden her eyes slid to Rick, who was standing quietly at the bottom of the stairs, and flicked away as she caught his glance. Schooling her face to absolute calmness, she stared down at the two police officers, and knew to the second when he looked away. There would be time enough for discussions about what had happened between them later; for now, mercifully, they would have to wait.

'Morning, miss.'

Turning back to Rick, the older of the two officers stared down at his open notebook for a second before he spoke.

'Now, just let's get this straight then. You've been here what...about two days now, is it?'

'Yes. We took shelter from the storm when Harriet's car ran out of petrol a couple of miles back down the road.'

There was an exchange of glances, then the officer flicked back through several pages of his notebook and stopped.

'That wouldn't be a Morris Traveller, would it, Miss?'

'Yes,' she answered, descending the stairs to the next but bottom tread. 'A yellow one. Have you found it?'

'Yes, though I'm afraid it's a write-off. Got swept away during the flood, so there'll be little you can do with it now.'

Harriet felt a great wave of sadness fill her. That old car had been part of her life for so long now, she was going to miss her.

'Now, if you'll just let me have your names, then we can arrange to send a boat out in an hour or so to get you. We're full up, I'm afraid. You first, Miss...'

'Prince, Harriet Prince,' she replied automatically, her mind still full of the car's watery fate. He nodded, writing rapidly in his book before turning to Rick.

'And you, sir?'

'Rick Dawson.'

His voice was low, almost curt in its brevity, and Harriet shot him a swift glance, startled at the tone.

'Dawson...that wouldn't be James Merrick Dawson, would it, sir?'

There was a change to the policeman's voice now, a hint of formality which surprised her almost as much as what he'd just said. Opening her mouth, she started to tell him he was mistaken, when Rick spoke, his voice unmistakably clear.

'Yes, that's right.'

What did he mean, what on earth was he saying? Why, everyone knew that James Merrick Dawson was a world-famous producer whose films were instant box-office hits, not some struggling actor!

'But Ri——'

Harriet went to ask him what he was playing at when the second officer spoke, words that would be etched into her memory for ever.

'Well, are we glad to find you, sir. There's been quite a hunt going on for you this past couple of days, quite a few people worried where you'd got to, especially your wife!'

She had to keep busy, had to keep her hands and mind occupied, otherwise she knew she'd break down and cry. Working feverishly, Harriet packed tins into an old brown carton and carried it down the stairs to the kitchen, her heart leaping painfully in her chest as Rick appeared in the open doorway.

'We've got to talk, Harriet,' he said harshly, his face grim.

'Talk? About what . . . the wife you seem to have for-gotten, or the multi-million pound company you can lay claim to? Come on, Rick, you tell me what we've got to talk about.'

Pushing past him, she strode across the kitchen and started to stack the groceries back into the cupboard with little regard for any order. Outside she might be a spitting bundle of fury, but inside Harriet knew she was crying, crying silent sobs for the way he'd deceived her.

'For heaven's sake, woman, leave that!'

Crossing the room in two long strides, he wrenched the box from her hands and tossed it on to the counter, scattering tins with a clatter which made her flinch. Grasping hold of her arms, he held her in front of him, his eyes boring down into hers with an angry glitter in their depths.

'We have to talk about us, Harriet, and you know it.'

'*Us?* What do you mean, us? There is no "us", Mr Dawson. That's as much a figment of your imagination as the last role you played as a struggling actor.'

She twisted free and tried to push past him and escape back up the stairs, but he barred her way.

'I never said I was an actor,' he said with a forced calmness. 'That was just the interpretation you put on it.'

'Which you did nothing to disabuse me of,' she retorted hotly. 'Oh, how you must have laughed at me, laughed at my clumsy attempts to lend you money, when you could buy and sell someone like me ten thousand times over!'

'I never laughed, Harriet, not then, not now.'

'No?' Folding her arms, she held on to her control with a rigid determination, refusing to give in to the tears which filled her. 'So you didn't laugh...how nice! Didn't laugh either, I expect, when I fell in so readily with all your plans.'

'What do you mean?'

Standing straight, he glowered back at her, but she refused to be intimidated into silence.

'That little matter of a challenge, that's what I mean. Surely you've not forgotten about it, have you? No, I can see you haven't. You set out quite deliberately to make me like you, to make me find you attractive, and it appears you succeeded. Yes, you won, Rick Dawson, it's your victory, but somehow I think you'll find it's hollow. Now, if you'll excuse me, there are a few more things which need clearing away before we return to civilisation. After all, we don't want to keep either the police or your wife waiting, do we?'

Pushing past him with a force which would have startled her if she'd been half-rational, she fled back up the stairs and into her room, slamming the door behind her. Stripping off the clothes she'd borrowed, she folded them neatly before stowing them back into the dresser drawers. Her own jeans and sweatshirt were still damp, but Harriet hardly noticed as she pulled them on, one thought and one only writhing inside her. Why had he done it ... why?

The door opened, bouncing back on its hinges, the handle gouging a piece out of the plaster as it hit the wall, and she gasped in swift alarm. Rick stood in the doorway, face set, eyes cold in the stern mask of his face, and just for the tiniest of moments she felt a shiver of real fear race through her that maybe she'd pushed him that bit too far. However, there was no way she was going to back down, no way she was going to grovel when he was in the wrong; spinning round, she faced him squarely, her face pale.

'Get out!'

'I'm not leaving till you listen to some reason,' he said harshly.

Grasping the door, he swung it closed, leaning back against its surface, arms folded across his chest like a gaoler, and Harriet felt her heart start to hammer hard in her chest and turned away to hide her fear. Picking up the brush from the bedside-table, she pulled it roughly through her hair, her hands shaking so much that it snagged the silky strands and her eyes filled with tears.

'Don't,' he said softly.

He lifted the brush from her grasp and slowly worked the teeth free, his hands gentle against her scalp, so that for one brief moment time slipped backwards and she caught her breath in a tiny gasp of dismay. Taking the brush from him, she moved away and laid it back on the table, her fingers tracing over the faded pattern of leaves and flowers painted on its back in a light and strangely hesitant touch.

Was it real? Was she real? Was this whole crazy situation real? Or was it just some dreadful hallucination? She had to know, had to hear the truth of it all from his own lips. She turned to face him, her face pale, her hands now steady as she stared up at him.

'Just tell me one thing, just one, then we'll see if there is something we need to talk about.'

He nodded, his eyes expressionless in his set face and, taking a slow, deep breath, she said softly, 'Just tell me, Rick, that you're not married.'

There was a moment's pause, a second when hope flared to brief, glorious life, and then he spoke and that hope died a final, agonising death.

'I...I can't tell you that, Harriet. I'm sorry.'

His voice was low, filled with sadness and despair, but to Harriet it meant absolutely nothing, as the bitter anguish of true reality closed round her. She stared into his face, her eyes hollow in her pale face.

'Then there's nothing more to be said, is there?'

And, brushing past him, she walked from the room and down the stairs.

* * *

To Harriet the journey to the nearby town seemed to last for ever, but in truth it took barely twenty minutes. Sitting rigidly still in the shallow boat, she stared over the flat, unmoving grey water with unseeing eyes, her every thought and feeling caught up in the pain of what had happened. It wasn't only the shock of finding out that Rick was married which hurt her, it was the way he'd deceived her, letting her believe he was someone other than James Merrick Dawson, multi-millionaire producer. How could he have done it, how could he have cared so little to trick her that way? The questions spun round and round in her head till she felt dizzy, but when eventually they reached the edge of the town where the floodwater petered out, she was still no closer to an answer and doubted if she ever would be. The only person who knew why he'd done it was Rick himself and she would never ask him; pride would never let her do such a thing.

Rolling up the legs of her damp jeans, she climbed from the boat and waded to solid ground, ignoring the hand Rick held out to help her. She didn't need his help, didn't need anything at all from him now. Standing stiffly on the marshy ground, she forced a smile and murmur of thanks for the two elderly men who'd rowed them back, then turned and headed in the direction of town, uncaring if he followed. All she wanted now was to get home as soon as she could and put the whole of this nightmare incident behind her, though instinct told her it would never be that easy. There was no way she could dismiss the pain and anguish she was feeling by just setting some distance between herself and Rick Dawson, no way at all, but she had to try, had to make herself believe it was possible. If she didn't, then she had the feeling that life might prove unbearable in the future.

'Harriet, wait. How are you going to get home without the car?'

It was something which had just never occurred to her on the journey back, but now she would have to think about it and fast. With Betsy and all her luggage gone, and nothing more than a couple of pounds in the pocket of her jeans, she was going to be hard-pushed to get herself home this side of next year, but there was no way she was going to let him know that. She'd find a way, somehow, and without any help from him!

'I'll manage,' she said briefly, her voice cold.

'How?'

Grabbing her arm, Rick swung her round, his eyes running over her pale, set face with a strange expression in their depths, but Harriet was too filled with her own pain to care what he was feeling, and she pulled away.

'I said I'll manage and I will, so don't worry about it. I think it's rather too late to start worrying about me now, don't you?'

Bitterness tinged her voice, but she was past caring if he heard it and strode on towards the group of buildings which marked the centre of the small town. The church clock was striking, the low, sweet sound rolling over the still, damp air, and she automatically counted the strokes, a flare of amazement rising inside her as she realised it was only twelve o'clock. Was it only an hour and a half since that knock had come at the door, a bare ninety minutes since her whole world had been turned upside-down and set spinning? It must be, but in that brief time she seemed to have aged a lifetime. Never again would she rely on trust or instinct to judge a person...never. It had been a bitter lesson, but one Rick had taught her well.

'The police want us to call in at the station before we leave,' he said quietly. 'I believe it's over there, next to the church.'

She nodded, not trusting herself to speak, and followed him across the street, uncaring of the curious glances they were collecting. With their filthy, river-stained clothing, they must look like tramps, but appearance was the last thing she was concerned about at the moment. No, what she had to concentrate on now was getting through the next few minutes till she could make her escape and leave both this town and Rick Dawson behind her. She never wanted to see either of them again...ever!

CHAPTER NINE

HOURS later, Harriet unlocked the door to her house and walked slowly inside, her whole body aching with tiredness. It had taken all afternoon and the best part of the evening to get home by a complicated network of buses, but at last she'd made it. Closing the door gently, she walked along the hall and into the kitchen, automatically filling the kettle with water before setting it on the hob to boil. Although it had been hours since she'd last eaten, she didn't feel hungry, didn't think she could face even the smallest amount of food without feeling queasy. All she wanted to do was have a drink, then get to bed and try to put the whole of this horrible day behind her. As days went, this could definitely win an award for the worst one ever!

Sitting down on the padded rocker, she leant back and closed her eyes while she waited for the water to come to the boil. She was so tired that she could feel her body trembling with exhaustion, could feel the room swaying as though she was still making that dreadful journey along all those endless country lanes. Breathing deeply, she forced herself to relax, though she knew it would need more than just an extra boost of oxygen to ease the tension from her limbs and the memories from her mind.

The kettle boiled, the faint new-born whistle reaching to screaming pitch before she could summon up enough energy to leave the chair and switch off the gas. Spooning granules of instant coffee into a mug, she poured on the steaming water and stirred the dark liquid, leaving it black in the hope it would chase some of her tiredness away. There was a light tapping on the half-glassed back door, and setting the hot coffee down on the table she went to answer it, peering through the gloom at the stocky male figure standing outside.

'When did you get back? I wasn't expecting you till the end of the week.'

'Hello, Ken, come in,' she said quietly.

She walked back inside, leaving him to close the door and follow her into the room. Spooning coffee into a mug, she made a second drink before answering his question.

'I got back about ten minutes ago. Here, and mind, it's very hot.'

'Thanks. You look absolutely exhausted, love. What's happened?'

Sipping gingerly at the burning-hot coffee, Ken leant against the edge of the table, studying her with undisguised concern, and Harriet forced a smile to her tired lips. There was no way she wanted Ken worrying about her, no way she wanted him asking a heap of questions she'd rather not answer while everything was still so painfully raw at the moment. Maybe later she'd want to confide in him, but not now.

'I got lost on the way down and ended up getting caught in the floods.'

'Oh, no! I saw something about floods on the news, but never realised you'd get caught up in them. Are you all right?'

'Yes, fine. Just rather tired at the moment though I'm afraid Betsy wasn't so lucky.'

'Why, what happened?'

Pulling out a chair, Ken sat down and made himself comfortable, and Harriet tried not to groan aloud in dismay. The last thing she felt like doing at the moment was entertaining, but there was no way she could be rude and ask Ken to leave. He'd been a good friend to her over the years, and she certainly didn't want to offend him.

'Well, I not only got lost on the way down, but ran out of petrol, so I had to abandon the car in a lane while I took shelter in an empty house a couple of miles away. The police told me the car had been washed away by the floodwater, and that it's now a write-off.'

'What a shame,' he murmured sympathetically, 'but still, looking on the bright side, at least you weren't still in it when it happened.'

'I suppose you're right.'

'I know I am,' he said firmly. 'So how did the boys get on, have you heard?'

'Yes. I was able to ring through to Pat from the police station this morning, and fortunately they're all fine. Evidently the campsite is on high ground, so there was never any danger of them getting trapped by the floods. In fact, the only inconvenience they've suffered has been a lack of daily papers, so they've not done too badly,' she said wryly, and Ken laughed.

'And are you going back again to help out, or what?'

'No,' Harriet said firmly, knowing there was no way she could ever face making that journey again. 'No, Pat said I mustn't bother as they could manage without us. Evidently there's another local pack there from Ormskirk, so they've joined forces with them and there's quite enough adults to supervise all the boys.'

'Us? There was someone else trapped with you, then, Harriet?' Ken asked, standing up to cross the kitchen and rinse his mug under the tap. Harriet thanked heaven for the fact his back was towards her as she answered quietly.

'Yes. The uncle of one of the boys was with me.'

'Well, at least you had some company, then, love,' Ken said, turning to smile at her. 'At least you weren't alone.'

'No,' she answered softly. 'No, I wasn't alone.'

She slept heavily that night, her mind and body totally exhausted by all the traumas of the day, but when eventually she awoke she felt little better. Pulling on a pair of old worn cords and a thin sweater, she went downstairs and let herself out into the garden, feeling the warmth of the sun shiver over her cold body. Staring down the length of the long garden and up the green slope of land to Ashurst Beacon, she tried to collect her thoughts together just enough to plan the day, but somehow it seemed impossible while this aching feeling of betrayal numbed her body.

Why had he done it? Why? The question rippled endlessly round her head in circles, but still there was no answer to chase it away, nothing which could make her understand his actions. What she'd felt for Rick had been not only physical attraction, but tenderness and caring; he'd awoken a spark in her which deep down she knew would be nigh on impossible to snuff out. She'd thought he'd felt the same about her, but obviously she'd been wrong, very wrong. He'd felt nothing for her, he'd just used her and she had to face it.

The telephone rang, the strident tone cutting through her unhappy thoughts, and with a weary sigh she went back inside to answer it. She pushed the clinging curls back from her face as she lifted the receiver.

'Hello.'

'Harriet? It's Rick.'

The shock of hearing his voice made her stagger so that she clutched at the wall, all colour draining from her face, leaving it as waxenly pale as a lily.

'Hello? Harriet, can you hear me?'

Concern tinged his voice now, but Harriet scarcely heard it as desperately she tried to cling on to what little remained of her composure. Tears were massing at the back of her eyes, but she refused to give in to them, refused to let him know what sweet agony it was to hear his voice. She had to remember the one plain, stark, cold fact that he was married!

The thought steadied her, gave her the strength to answer, though her voice trembled as she spoke.

'What do you want?'

'I . . . I just wanted to check you'd got home safely,' he answered briefly, his voice so low that she could barely hear it.

'Well, as you can hear, I did.'

'Good. I was worried about you.'

'Were you? Why, how nice.' Sarcasm edged her words, but she didn't care, didn't care about anything except hanging on to her composure. 'Well, if that's all you wanted . . .'

'Harriet! Wait! Don't hang up, please.'

'Why, what else is there to say, Rick? I thought we'd said everything there was to be said yesterday.'

'I know, but I just had to speak to you, had to make you understand that I never meant any of it to turn out how it did.'

'I see, and you think that's going to make all the difference, do you? The fact that you never really meant any of it to happen?'

'Damn it, woman, of course it should make a difference. You're implying that I deliberately set out to deceive you, but it's just not true. Everything just happened, nothing was planned, even our lovemaking, and as far as I remember you were far from unwilling then, were you?'

That hurt, driving the knife right through to the bone, but Harriet was suddenly too caught up by anger to feel the pain.

'Yes, I was willing and I don't deny it; willing to go to bed with you, willing almost to fall in love with you, but then it wasn't really you I wanted, was it?'

'What do you mean, it wasn't me? What the hell are you talking about?' Anger rippled through his deep voice, but Harriet couldn't give a damn. All she knew was that she wanted to hurt him, as much as he'd hurt her.

'I mean that the man I was attracted to back at that house, the man I held in my arms that night, doesn't really exist. It was Rick Dawson, unknown struggling actor I wanted, not James Merrick Dawson, world-famous producer. Yes, you deceived me, tricked me by letting me believe you were really a different person, but now I know that man just doesn't exist. So go back to your wife, *Mr Dawson* . . . she's the one you should be concerned about now, not me. I don't even know you!'

Slowly, gently, she replaced the receiver and, resting her head against the cold, hard wall, let all the pent-up tears flow as she cried for a man who had never been real except, maybe, in her heart.

Summer drifted in with a soft, warm brilliance which did little to melt the ice which seemed to encase Harriet's heart. She felt numb, as though all the pain and anguish had melded together to form one huge lump of greyness which weighed her down. Working, talking, sleeping, walking... everything she did seemed to be tinged with this same drab shade, as though all the colour had been drained away. Pushing herself to the absolute limit, where the next step meant total exhaustion, she tried to force the feeling away, but nothing seemed to be able to break through its hold.

All around her life went on as normal. Pat returned from camp with the boys, and accepted her brief explanation of what had happened with sympathetic murmurs and just the tiniest hint of curiosity which Harriet did nothing to appease. Jill and Dave, golden and glowing with health, arrived back from their holiday, so full of all they'd seen and done that they never seemed to notice that her interest was more forced than genuine. Yes, life flowed on, but inside Harriet felt as though she was slowly dying.

Night after long night she would awake and lie sleeplessly in her bed, tossing the memories endlessly round in her head, but nothing could ever change what had happened. True, Rick had told her he'd not planned any of it, but why should she believe him? He'd made a complete and utter fool of her, and her only consolation lay in the fact that no one other than them knew about it.

At first she'd been worried that the Press would find out what had happened and that all the details of the two days they'd spent together would be dug up and raked over for public inspection, but after scouring the papers day after day she'd come to realise her fears were groundless. Somehow, by using whatever influence he had, he'd found a way to cover up the story, though bitterness welled inside her as she realised it wouldn't be for her sake that he'd bothered, but his wife's. After all, to James Merrick Dawson, man of wealth and means, she meant absolutely nothing.

It was a painful thought, and one Harriet knew should have made her hate him, but even hate couldn't force a way through the grey veil. So life went on, and on the outside she appeared just the same, but inside, day by day, the greyness turned a little darker and a thicker layer of ice formed round her heart.

A month or so after she'd returned home, Harriet was sitting in the kitchen attempting to work. In the rocking chair Caspar was curled up into a snug ball, snoring gently, the low, soft sound filling the quiet room with its gentle rhythm. It was the sort of peaceful day, in fact, that she used to dream of, but now, for some strange reason, she found it irritating and unsettling. Tearing the part-finished sketch from her pad, she screwed it into a tight ball and tossed it aside with a grimace, knowing there was no way she could submit such poor work to the paper. Pushing back her chair, she stood up and crossed to the window, staring with unseeing eyes down the length of the garden.

She'd been finding it increasingly difficult to work for the past few days now, finding that ideas, though good, just wouldn't translate to paper, and frankly it worried her. Granted, she had enough material stockpiled to last her six months if need be, but that wasn't the point. If she couldn't draw, couldn't find some measure of satisfaction in her work, then just what did she have in her life? Nothing. It was a frightening thought, and one which had started to haunt her.

The clatter of the letterbox opening mercifully disturbed the depressing train of thoughts, and hurrying from the room Harriet went to see what had been delivered, a tiny spurt of curiosity rising inside her as she spotted the long, cream envelope lying in solitary splendour on the mat. She stared down at the type-written address for a second before easing her thumb under the flap and peeling it open. The folded sheet of matching paper was equally impressive with its gold embossed heading, and smoothing it carefully out Harriet skimmed her eyes over it, pleasure surging through her as she realised that here in her hand she held the promise of a dream. She crossed the hall and, sitting down on the bottom of the stairs, read the few brief paragraphs again more slowly, frightened that she'd made some sort of crazy mistake in that first swift perusal. However, even a dozen or so re-reads came out the same, and a sudden smile softened the tight drawn line of her lips as she realised it.

'Well, it's nice to see you looking so happy for once; what's happened?'

Jill had let herself in through the back door, making her way quietly along the hall to find her, and Harriet jumped as she heard her voice.

'Oh, you startled me! I didn't hear you come in. Look, this has just come. What do you think?'

Holding the letter out to her sister, Harriet waited while she read it, her brow puckering into a small, nervous frown as she waited for her comments.

'Think? Why, I think it's wonderful, of course. Oh, Harriet, it's what you've always dreamed of, isn't it?'

Jill studied her for a second, eyes alight with pleasure, and suddenly Harriet laughed.

'Yes . . . yes, of course it is, but I just can't believe it's real!'

'Well, it is. It's here in beautiful black and white, so just you believe it. Listen——' Glancing down at the paper, Jill found the place she wanted and read slowly, savouring every word. ' "Please contact me at the above address so that we can arrange to meet and discuss the possibility of turning your cartoon, *King Caspar the Cat*, into a feature-length film. Yours sincerely, Jason Fane." You really can't get plainer than that, now can you, Harry?'

'No, no, of course you're right. Oh, Jill, wouldn't it be wonderful?' For the first time in weeks, happiness radiated from her, so that for a moment she looked more like herself than she'd done for ages, a fact which Jill noted but refrained from mentioning.

'It would, indeed. So what are you waiting for? Why don't you ring now and make that appointment?'

'Well, I . . . I . . .' Harriet hesitated, the smile fading as quickly from her lips as it had come, driven away by a sudden sharp wave of fear. All she'd gone through these past few weeks had taken its toll on her confidence, so that now she felt suddenly uncertain of her own ability to cope with what would be a new untried venture. What if she couldn't come up with what they wanted? What if none of it turned out how it should? What if they decided not to make the film, after all? Could she handle the disappointment? Caught in a strange limbo of uncertainty, Harriet stood in the centre of the cool, bright hall, a thousand fleeting emotions crossing her mobile face as she wrestled with the decision, till slowly it came to her that there was no going back to life as it once had been. For weeks she'd felt like a zombie, merely going through the motions of living, but now she knew it was time to make a decision. She couldn't go on drifting like this forever, she had to come to terms with what had happened, had to make herself accept the fact that all the pain and anguish was just another part of living.

There was no way she could stay locked within her own little world, cowering away from everything new in case it hurt her. She had to go on, had to make a life for herself, and maybe, one day in the future, find a man who could make her burn as Rick had once so briefly done. She'd taken a blow and it had been a hard one, but she had to fight back. If she didn't, then she may as well be dead.

She met Jill's eyes across the narrow width of the hallway, her face now calm and quietly determined.

'I'll go and phone now. As you say, what's the point in waiting.'

She walked through to the kitchen and slowly, carefully dialled the number to begin her life anew.

Jason Fane was a man of medium height, medium build and boundless energy. After twenty minutes in his company, Harriet felt totally exhausted, exhausted but filled with a strange new flood of enthusiasm. The fact that he'd thought deeply about turning the cartoon serial into a full-length film was obvious from the outset, as was the fact that he'd researched her work thoroughly. The file on his desk was filled almost to overflowing with cuttings from various papers, many of which she'd forgotten about. A lot of time and effort had been put into the research, and Harriet wouldn't have been human if she'd not felt flattered by such obvious interest. Sitting comfortably on the soft deep sofa in his London office, she suddenly knew that she'd made the right decision in coming. Just hearing him talk, hearing him outline what they'd need from her to do the film and make it a success, was already bringing a warmth back into her life which had been missing far too long. Yes, doing this film could prove to be her salvation.

'So that's it, Harriet, what do you think? Are you interested?' Leaning forward, hands loosely clasped round his knee, Jason studied her closely, his eyes intent as they scoured over her face. 'Look, I know I shouldn't rush you like this; you probably need time to think about it, but I'd really like to know if you're even half-way interested.'

She was interested, *very* interested, and the Harriet of a few weeks ago would have rushed to say so, but now she was inclined to treat things with a lot more caution. After all, there were a lot of things which needed considering, as he'd said, and if there were pitfalls to the project—well, she wanted to know what they were now, before she fell right in. She'd taken enough knocks recently by being too trusting to want to take any more than were quite unavoidable.

'Well?' Impatiently he leant further forwards, and Harriet smiled, finding his enthusiasm infectious.

'Yes, I'm interested,' she replied steadily. 'To be quite honest, it's something I've always dreamed of, but there's still a lot of things I want to know before I make a final committment.'

'Of course, I can understand that. You'd be a fool not to go into it from every angle, and I promise you that we'll cover all the details you want to. After all, if this takes off, then you stand to make a lot of money from it, and you'd be mad not to make some sort of safeguards. I suggest that we draw up a preliminary contract and you get your solicitor to go through it, eh?'

With half the battle won he leant back in his chair, some of the nervous tension easing from his body. In his late thirties, he had the sort of easy confidence and dark good looks which Harriet knew would attract women by the dozen, but looking at him she knew that not even the tiniest hint of attraction stirred to life inside her. She'd been spoiled for that by a blond-haired man with green eyes like emeralds.

The thought was unsettling, and she quickly wrenched her mind away from it, back to what could be her future. Suddenly she knew with a strange, deep-seated conviction that the future lay along the lines Jason Fane had just suggested. She'd do the film, let Caspar become a national hero if he was meant to, and see which way her life moved on from there. There was no going back, not now, not ever.

'I'll do it,' she said quietly.

'You will? Why, that's marvellous; really marvellous! I can't tell you how pleased I am. I knew as soon as I was shown your work that it was just what we were looking for, and now I can only say how pleased I am that you've decided to come in on the project. It's going to be big, Harriet, I can sense it, really big.'

He caught her hand in his and held it, his eyes looking deep into hers for a few moments before he continued softly, 'And do you know what's going to be the best thing about it all?'

'What?' she asked, letting her hand rest quietly in his.

'That it will give us a chance to get to know one another.'

There was just the hint of a promise in his voice, a promise that dozen or so women would have jumped at, but, pulling her hand gently free, Harriet knew that to her it meant absolutely nothing.

The work was long, hard and rigorously taxing, but to Harriet it was an absolute godsend, keeping her mind and body occupied from sunrise to sunset so that she had little time left to dwell on all that had happened. At

Jason's insistence she'd moved down from her home in Upholland and rented a flat on the outskirts of London, knowing he was right when he said she needed to be close at hand during every stage of the production.

Although she wasn't doing the drawing herself, an impossible task for just one person when several hundred sketches might be needed to complete just one moving frame, she had agreed to be there as consultant for the team of artists whose job it was to translate it all to paper. Watching them work, watching the painstaking care, the attention to detail that was needed, she was filled with admiration for their skill. Every single line had to be drawn by hand, then painted using a complicated cross-reference system of colours. Tints were numbered and carefully labelled so that no mistake could be made which might cost the production company thousands of pounds in delay. As Jason wryly pointed out when she queried the need for all this care, there would always be someone, somewhere, who'd notice that the sky was a different shade of blue, or that Caspar's fur was a darker shade of grey in one frame than the next. Every possibility just had to be covered.

Between her and Jason there soon sprang up a close working relationship based on mutual respect, and on his behalf a very healthy measure of interest in Harriet as a woman. Every day, and often far into the early hours of the morning, they worked together on the project, and soon Harriet knew that he was starting to feel more than just a friendly interest in her. Nothing was ever said, nothing ever put into so many words, but she could sense it and at first had even tried to match it. But, no matter how much she might want to feel something more than friendship for him, it seemed to make very little difference. It was as though her whole ability to feel anything deeper had gone, been wiped away for ever by that one brief, burning rage of feeling she'd felt for Rick Dawson. Would she always feel like this, always feel as though part of her had died? She didn't know, didn't even dare to dwell on it in case the prospect became too bleak for her to cope with.

Several weeks after she'd started work on the project, Harriet was in the small bedroom of the flat, getting ready for a rare evening out. To her mind, being more used to the demanding deadlines of newspapers, the film seemed to be progressing with extreme slowness, but to Jason it was all moving along beautifully. Everything was way ahead of schedule, he'd assured her, and used this statement as the basis of his argument to take a night off and go out for dinner. It would do them both good, stop them from becoming bored and boring, he'd insisted, and in his usual high-handed manner had overridden all her rather lame excuses. Now Harriet had to admit that she was looking forward to a night on the town, a pleasant change from the way she usually spent any free time, slumped in front of the television.

The doorbell rang and, skimming a quick look into the mirror, she pushed one last stray red curl back up into the loose knot on top of her head. She'd let her hair grow these last few months, and now it reached just past her shoulders in a riotous tumble of rich auburn waves, but for tonight's outing she'd pinned it up, exposing the long, slim line of her throat and the soft, pale curve of her shoulders. She was looking good and she knew it, her body reed-slim in the clinging black dress, her make-up immaculately perfect, so why did she have a sudden mental image of herself dressed in a hideous floral frock, her hair ruffled, her legs bare and grimy? And why did she suddenly wish she looked that way again? It didn't make sense.

The bell rang again, a barely concealed impatience in its swiftly repeated tones, and with a shrug she pushed the image from her mind. That girl and that time were gone now, forever. Hurrying from the room, she pulled open the front door and glared with mock ferocity at the man leaning against the door-frame, one finger stabbing at the bellpush.

'May I ask what you think you're doing by ringing like that?' she demanded haughtily.

Jason grinned, his handsome face creasing into a smile which held little hint of apology.

'Lady, be glad I didn't break your door down. I'd begun to think you'd got cold feet and decided not to come.'

'Do I look as if I'm ready to spend the evening at home in front of the television?' she asked with a laugh. 'This is hardly the outfit for it, surely?'

Following the sweep of her hand, his dark eyes skimmed down the slender length of her body in the clinging dress, and all the laughter faded abruptly from his eyes. Tension fizzled through the air, and immediately Harriet regretted her teasing. She liked and admired Jason Fane far too much to lead him on and let him hope for something she could never give him.

'Harriet . . .'

'I'll just get my wrap, Jason. I won't be a minute.'

Hurrying back to the bedroom, she caught up the soft, beaded wrap and threw it round her bare shoulders, her hands trembling with a sudden attack of nerves. The time was fast coming when she would have to make Jason understand her feelings, and she dreaded it, dreaded the fact that she might lose him as a friend, dreaded, too, the possibility that she might hurt him. She knew too much about that sort of hurt to want to inflict it on anyone else.

'You'll have to stop running some time, you know, Harriet.'

Lounging against the open door to the bedroom, Jason stared at her, his eyes dark and filled with a quiet determination. Looking up, she gave a small, nervous laugh which didn't fool either one of them for a moment.

'I really don't know what you mean, Jason. Now, come on, or are you trying to weasel out of buying me dinner?'

Picking up her bag, she crossed the room and went to walk past him, stopping as he caught her arm in a light clasp.

'Who was it, Harriet? Who was it who hurt you?'

The question hung in the air for a second, but Harriet knew there was no way she could gather it in and give him an answer. She smiled as she pulled free, her face filled with a brittle amusement.

'No one Jason. Absolutely no one. The man who hurt me doesn't even exist!'

And she walked from the room, leaving the words to echo round the lonely space.

CHAPTER TEN

DESPITE its rather shaky start, the evening was a great success, but left Harriet feeling totally exhausted. Jason was as full of energy in his play as in his work, and it had been she who'd finally admitted defeat and begged to be taken home in the early hours of the morning. Now, the day after their night on the town, she was feeling decidedly sluggish. The temptation to just put her tired head down on the edge of her desk and sleep was so great that she could actually feel herself leaning forwards till she made an almighty effort to resist.

This morning she was working in the basement studio, wrestling with one small scene which seemed to be causing everyone a vast amount of trouble. At the far side of the room several of the production artists were working, the quiet sound of their voices just filtering down the length of the room to where she sat staring into space. For some reason she was finding it very difficult to get down on to paper just what she wanted; there was a particular expression she needed for the cartoon Caspar which just wouldn't come, and not for the first time she wished she could have brought the real one down to London with her for inspiration. However, deep down, she knew that he would never be happy cooped up in the flat all day away from all his favourite haunts, and that she'd been right to accept Ken's offer to mind him till she went back. And she would go back, of that, at least, she was certain. Oh, London was exciting, the hustle and bustle of city life invigorating, but it wasn't home and she was beginning to think rather longingly of the green Lancashire countryside and all her friends and family. Yes, she would go back, but not till this project was completed, and if she didn't get a move on with this scene then that mightn't be till she was drawing her old-age pension! There had to be something which could solve her problem and get her brain cells working.

Thinking quickly, Harriet ran her mind back over all the cartoons she'd done in the past few months, trying to remember if any of them had contained something similar which she could now crib from. Nothing came to mind and, picking up the pen, she was about to make yet another attempt at getting just the right curl to Caspar's haughty lip when suddenly she remembered the thick file of her work which Jason kept in his office. Maybe it would be worth snatching a glance at some of those sketches to see if they could jog her memory.

Picking up a small pad and pencil, she left the room, and after sparing just one swift glance for the spiralling flight of stairs quickly punched the button for the lift. She felt far too fragile at the moment for that much healthy exercise; it could wait till she was feeling stronger!

Jason's office was on the sixth floor of the imposing modern building, and at this time of the day everywhere was nearly deserted, apart from a handful of staff covering the lunch hour. Nodding to the girl who was guarding the outer office, Harriet knocked briefly on his door and stepped inside to find the room empty. From the direction of one of the side rooms came the sound of muted laughter, and Harriet grinned as she realised that, far from feeling wrung out as she was, Jason must feel up to entertaining. Where he got his energy from was a complete and total mystery, one she wished he'd share with her right at this very moment!

For a moment she considered popping through to ask him for the file, then swiftly decided not to bother. After all, she knew exactly where he kept it, knew too that he would never mind her getting it herself. She pulled open the bottom drawer of the tall filing cabinet and drew out the stiff, thick green folder, spreading it out on the desk while she skimmed quickly through its contents. Several of the cartoons were ages old, and Harriet had to stifle a chuckle as she now viewed them, realising just how much her technique had improved in recent years. Carefully and methodically she worked her way through the pile, a weary sigh leaving her lips as she realised that not one of them was just what she wanted. Still, a few had refreshed her mind about other points, so maybe the time hadn't been entirely wasted.

Picking up the pile of cuttings, she patted them back into some semblance of order and started to slip them back into the folder, pausing as her eyes suddenly caught sight of the thick pad of creamy paper tucked in the very bottom. It looked vaguely familiar, but just for the moment she couldn't place it. Setting the cuttings aside, she pulled it out and flipped it open...and the breath caught in her throat as she realised just what she was holding.

Time stood still, then rolled swiftly backwards to the last time she'd held this pad of creamy-pale paper all those months before, when she'd sat drawing in the bedroom of the flooded house. Hands trembling, she flicked through the pages one by one, her eyes scouring every sketch, desperate to find that she'd been mistaken. But there was no mistake; every line, every stroke, every patch of shading was just as she'd once drawn it. Where had it come from...and how had Jason got hold of it?

There was a sudden flare of noise, the sound of a door opening, footsteps entering the room and laughter abruptly halted as Harriet spoke, her voice trembling as she stared down at the paper.

'Where did you get this, Jason—just tell me, where?'

There was silence, a hard, thick silence which grated on her overstretched nerves, so that impatiently she started to repeat the question, then stopped as someone else supplied the answer.

'I gave it to him, Harriet.'

The voice was the same, just as she remembered it, just as she'd heard it so many times in her head every one of these long, lonely days and even longer, lonelier nights, and her body went cold with sudden icy fear. She stared across the room into the face of Rick Dawson and knew that life had just come full circle, and the old had merged with the new.

A bare hour later Harriet was sitting quietly in the boardroom while all around her chaos reigned. Raised voices filled the air, assaulting her ears with their harsh sound, and in a sudden flash of impatience she realised she'd had enough. She let her eyes skim over each one of the men in turn, ignoring the blond man who was standing alone by the window. Most of the men she knew already, knew they were big wheels in the hierarchy of the film company, but frankly, right at this moment, she couldn't give a damn just who they were exactly.

For this past hour, ever since she'd made her declaration that she wasn't prepared to go on with the film and Jason had convened this impromptu meeting, she'd listened, first to their pleas, then their arguments, and latterly their threats, and now she wasn't prepared to listen any longer.

'Gentlemen!'

Raising her voice above the hubbub, Harriet cut off all the noise with one word, then stood up, her hands resting on the edge of the huge smoked-glass table. She pinned each man in turn with a cold stare before letting her gaze rest finally on Jason. Colour flared under his dark skin, but Harriet was still too hurt and incensed by what had happened to care if she upset him. When she spoke, her voice was low but tinged with so much finality that no one hearing it could doubt she meant every word.

'I want out, now, and I don't give a damn what you threaten me with for breaking the contract. There is no way I am going to do anything further on this film, no way I would have even agreed to consider it if I'd been given all the facts at the beginning. You have my full permission to carry on and use the cartoon, but I want no further part in any of it. Is that clear?'

There was silence which lasted the bare ten seconds Harriet was prepared to give them, a silence she had the feeling which owed more to shock than agreement.

'Good. Now, gentlemen, that's it. If there are any further details which need sorting out, then please contact my solicitor. I shall no longer be available... to any of you!'

Picking up her bag, she turned and strode towards the door, her back and shoulders stiffly rigid. Inside she was crumbling, breaking into a thousand tiny pieces, but there was no way she was going to show it. As exits went this one was going to be 'A-plus' graded!

'Harriet, wait! Look, you can't just go like this... be reasonable.'

Jumping hastily to his feet, Jason tried to stop her, but she barely shortened her stride and just flung a reply over her shoulder. 'Oh, but I can, and I will, Jason—and there's no way you or anyone else is going to stop me.'

Sweeping past him, she headed for the lifts and punched the button, tapping her foot with impatience while she waited for it to arrive. At the moment anger was holding her together, but when that faded, as it must very shortly, then she wanted to be well away from this building and everyone in it. She wanted no reports of her breakdown to travel along the grapevine to the man at the very top, the big boss... Rick Dawson.

God, she'd been such a fool, such a stupid, blind little fool not to have realised it all before, not to have seen that someone must have had a hand in this project. After all, there were dozens of cartoons about, so why should hers have been selected above all the others? No, Rick Dawson had planned it all from the very beginning; got Jason to contact her, bait the hook, then reel her in till she was well and truly landed. Why he'd done it, she had no idea; and she hadn't wanted to stop long enough to ask him. No, all she knew was that once again he'd tricked her. He, James Merrick Dawson, might own the whole of this damned film company, but there was no way he was going to own her!

The lift still hadn't come, and with a muttered curse she swung away and strode along the carpeted corridor towards the staircase.

'Harriet, please let me explain. You seem to have got everything out of proportion.'

Jason hurried towards her, his voice holding a note of desperation, but Harriet had no kindness left to spare for anyone. As far as she was concerned, Jason Fane had been part of the conspiracy from the beginning, and she wanted nothing more to do with him.

'Harriet, wait! You must listen.'

Jason tried to halt her speedy departure by grasping her arm, but Harriet shrugged his hand off, her face cold as she shot him just one look.

'I don't have to do anything, Mr Fane. I'm no longer under contract to you, remember?'

'I know...I know, I heard you, and though I can't understand what it's all about, I respect your wish to end the contract. But don't go like this, Harriet. You seem to think there was some sort of plot going on, but it wasn't like that, believe me. OK, so Rick was the one who first showed me your work—and yes, he did ask me not to mention the fact—but frankly, if it hadn't been just what we were after then I would never have considered using it. Harriet, are you listening to me?'

'The lady's a poor listener, Jason; that's something you've got to learn about her.'

The low voice broke the spell, and Harriet swung round, icy scorn twisting her face as she stared at Rick who'd come so quietly along the corridor.

'Poor listener? Too damn right I'm a poor listener when it comes to lies, and that's all I've ever heard from you, Mr Dawson, isn't it? Lies and deceit piled one on top of the other, enough to build a skyscraper. To be honest, the only way I'd ever listen to another word you said is if you bound and gagged me!'

'Is that right? Well, maybe that can be arranged, lady.' There was a dangerous note to his voice, the soft purr of a tiger about to spring, and Harriet took a slow step backwards, reaching for the catch on the stair door and freedom. Rick was staring at her, a light in his green eyes which was frankly scary, and in a sudden rush she knew that she'd just pushed him over the limit. Maybe she should apologise, murmur a few soothing, meaningless phrases, but deep down she knew they'd probably choke her! No, her best bet now was to get away as fast as her legs could carry her.

The thought had hardly crossed her mind when he moved so fast that he caught her by surprise, and she gasped in stunned dismay as she felt herself being lifted and flung over his shoulder.

'Put me down!' she screamed, but he took not an atom of notice. Balling her hands into fists, she rained a shower of blows across the width of his shoulders, but he seemed impervious to her efforts and just held her even tighter.

'Rick, what the hell...?' Jason tried to catch his arm, but stopped as Rick swung round and snarled a warning, his eyes deadly in the harsh mask of his face.

'Keep out of this, Fane. This is between me and the lady. Now, get my car round to the back, and make it fast!'

Jason hesitated, his face twisted with indecision, and Harriet stopped her pounding and tried desperately to appeal to his reason.

'Jason, you can't let him do this. Make him put me down.'

She tried to break free of Rick's hold, but he just held her even tighter, her legs clamped against the hard muscles of his chest in a grip of iron.

'I...I...'

Looking from one to the other, Jason was obviously caught in the middle of a dilemma: he wanted to help Harriet, but the murderous look on Rick's face was enough to stop an army.

'Do it!' Rick ordered grimly and, pushing open the doors to the staircase, started to make his way downstairs.

'Rick, stop it! What do you think you're playing at?'

Tears of fury and fright were streaming down Harriet's face now, and with a shaking hand she tried to brush them away, then grabbed hold of his shoulders as he took a bend with more speed than was sensible. It was crazy, the whole unbelievable situation was crazy. This madman was making off with her down a crowded staircase, and no one, but no one was trying to stop him! It was the end of the lunch break and people were hurrying back to their offices, but instead of demanding to know what was happening they just stood aside and watched them! Maybe it was a good thing she'd just thrown up her contract, because it was certain she could never come back here again. Their exit from the building was going to be the high spot for the rest of the decade!

Reaching the bottom of the stairs, Rick shouldered his way through the fire doors and strode across the marble foyer, uncaring of the gasps which followed their progress, and Harriet hid her face in mortification, praying the ground would open up and swallow her. She had to make him put her down somehow. Forcing the anger from her voice, she tried to adopt a soothing tone, hoping to appeal to what little might be left of his reason.

'Rick, put me down . . . please.'

Her voice was filled with a nice touch of pleading entreaty, and just for a moment she felt him relax his grip a fraction. It was just the fraction she needed. With a quick twist, she nearly broke free, one foot just tip-toeing on the marble before he snatched her back and re-tightened his grip on her backside.

'No chance, Harriet, honey,' he murmured, his breath coming in laboured gasps. 'There's no way you're getting away from me now, d'you hear me? No way! I'm going to make you listen if it's the last thing I ever do!'

Pushing past the startled security guard, he strode down the final flight of steps into the basement car park, stopping next to a long, low maroon car in the aisle with its engine ticking over. Jason was standing next to it, his face grim and filled with a quiet sadness which suddenly stilled Harriet's frantic struggling. There was such an air of defeat about him, a dejection that made him look years older, that it pulled at her heartstrings for a moment. Dropping the keys into Rick's hand, he said, softly, 'I hadn't realised that Harriet was the woman, Rick. I wish you'd told me.'

He walked slowly up the stairs, leaving Harriet staring silently after him, wondering just what he'd meant.

'That's what it does to a man when he has to turn away from the woman he loves, Harriet,' Rick said softly.

His voice was low, without inflection, yet suddenly the air seemed to be charged with an electric tension that made her tingle from head to toe. There was a moment's stillness, as though the whole world stopped then shivered on its axis, as slowly Rick slid her down so that her feet touched the floor and held her loosely in the circle of his arms. She let her eyes run over his face, and something in his expression seemed to steal what was left of her breath away.

'Rick, I...'

'Shhh.' Raising his hand, he pressed it gently against her lips, his fingers warm and soft against her skin. 'Not now, Harriet, not just now. Later, when we've the time and the space. Do you remember when we were at the house, when you said you owed me for saving your life?

Well, I'm collecting now, Harriet, but will you pay? Will you come with me and just listen to what I have to say?'

'Yes,' she whispered. 'Yes, I'll pay.' And she felt the last drop of resistance drain slowly away.

They drove in silence, the powerful car eating up mile after long mile as they followed the roads out from the city and into the country. Leaning back in the soft leather seat, Harriet closed her eyes, filled with a sudden peace she hadn't felt for months. Where Rick was taking her she didn't know, didn't know either what he wanted from her, but for some strange reason she didn't care. All she knew was that it felt so good to have him next to her, to feel the soft brush of his arm against hers, to smell the faint, warm smell of cologne and clean skin which was intrinsically his. In some indefinable way she felt as though she'd just come home at the end of a long, terrifying journey.

'All right?'

His voice was soft, and Harriet looked up, a tiny smile curving her lips as she stared back at him, loving the way his green eyes stroked over her face in faint concern.

'Yes, fine.'

'Good. It's going to be a long drive, so why don't you see if you can sleep? You look so tired.'

'Mmm—are you implying I look a sight?' she asked with mock ferocity, her heart leaping in her chest as he answered softly.

'You could never look anything but beautiful to me, Harriet.'

Colour flared under her skin and she turned away quickly, frightened of what he might read in her face at that moment. Closing her eyes, she nestled down into the seat, feeling the softness enclose her body as one single thought enclosed her mind. She loved him. All these long months she'd fought against the knowledge, knowing deep down it had the power to destroy her, but now she could no longer fight the battle. Despite all that had happened, all the pain and anguish which had eaten at her night and day, she still loved him, and while it should have terrified her to admit it, somehow, strangely, it didn't. What would happen she didn't know, didn't know either if she could ever disclose her feelings to him. All she knew was that, somehow, just facing up to the knowledge had eased the pain.

The miles rolled on and Harriet slept, her head cushioned first against the soft leather and then against the firm muscles of Rick's shoulder as, unconsciously, she turned towards him. When she awoke the car had stopped and a soft blue-grey evening light was pouring in through the windscreen. She rubbed the sleep from her eyes and looked round, her gaze lingering on Rick who was sitting quietly smoking, his head resting against the door-frame.

'Why didn't you wake me?' she asked, suddenly confused and embarrassed to find herself pressed so close against him.

'You needed the sleep, and there's no hurry. From now on we've all the time in the world.' Stubbing out the cigarette, he turned towards her, gently pulling her into his arms, his eyes gleaming translucent green in the soft, dim light as they stared down into hers. 'From now on we can take as long as we like; we owe each other that much at least.' He pressed his lips to hers in a gentle, soft kiss, then pulled away. Harriet looked down, not wanting him to see just how much that brief contact had made her ache for something more.

'Shall we go in, then?' he asked, a touch of knowing amusement in his voice, and she nodded, not daring to speak in case she gave in to the sudden, overwhelming urge which rose up to tell him here and now how much she loved him. Opening the door, she stepped out and stopped, staring round her in stunned, disbelieving silence.

'So you've finally realised where we are,' he said with a laugh.

'Yes,' she whispered, turning dazed eyes towards him, 'but how... why...?'

'I own it, Harriet. It's mine now, all of it.'

'Yours?'

Turning in a slow circle, Harriet stared round the beautiful flower-filled garden down to the nearby river, and then on to the house, its grey stone mellow in the last dying rays of daylight... the house they'd been marooned in!

Laughing at her expression, Rick took her arm, leading her along the newly paved path and unlocking the fresh-painted white front door, pushing it wide so that she could precede him into the hall. Harriet had a sudden vivid impression of how it had looked when she'd last seen it—the paint peeling, the floor covered in a thick stinking layer of mud—then it was gone, wiped away by the charm of the present.

The floor had been relaid, the wooden blocks gleaming with a soft buffed sheen which reflected the huge vase of fragrant garden flowers standing on an antique table. The walls had been colour-washed in a delicate blue, the perfect background for the soft-toned watercolours grouped at intervals to break the bareness. The carpet covering the stair treads was a richer, deeper shade of blue which glowed jewel-like in the warm light from the wall lamps. Slowly, as though in a dream, she walked along the hall and peered in to each of the downstairs rooms, her eyes sweeping over the comfortable, attractive furnishings with a hint of wonder in them, before turning back to Rick. Then she said simply, 'It's beautiful, Rick...just as it should be.'

There was no doubting she meant every word, and he smiled, the trace of tension leaving his face, so that for a second he looked boyishly young and light-hearted. Stepping forwards, he pulled her into his arms and hugged her close, his lips brushing over the thick, rich mass of her hair in a tender, brief kiss.

'I'm so glad you like it, honey.'

'Oh, I do, Rick, really. But how long have you had it? When did you move in?'

There were a thousand questions she wanted to ask him, but with his body pressed against hers it was suddenly difficult to think just what they were.

'I bought it a few weeks after we left, but I've not moved in as yet. I've been waiting to see what you thought about it.'

'Me? Why, what have I got to do with it?'

A sudden nervous tension was building inside her, and Harriet pulled away, walking a few feet back down the hall to trace her fingers over the carvings on the small table.

'Everything, Harriet,' he replied softly. 'I bought this house for one reason and one alone...so that you and I could live here.' He stared at her, and Harriet felt her knees go suddenly weak in apprehension. What was he suggesting? What did he mean? Surely he couldn't...

Her mind closed on the thought, and she swallowed, feeling suddenly sick to the depths of her stomach. The scent of the roses and sweet peas massed in the huge copper vase was overpoweringly cloying, and she moved away, clutching her bag tightly in her icy fingers as she stared up the stairs towards the dark, shadowed landing.

'Well, Harriet, will you? Will you live here as my...'

She couldn't bear it, couldn't bear to hear him say the word her mind had already thought of—'mistress'! Swinging round, she faced him, pain etched on her pale, drawn features.

'Damn you, Rick Dawson, damn you to hell for bringing me here and suggesting that! No, I won't live here with you, hidden away from the world while you spare me a tiny part of your life, the scraps you've got left over. No...no...*no*!'

She went to stride down the hall, but he stepped forwards and barred her way, his face harsh with a burning anger.

'What the hell are you talking about, "hidden away" while I spare you scraps of my life? I'm asking you to marry me, Harriet, to marry me and live here in this house while we make a life together—but if that's not enough, then just forget I ever spoke.'

'Marry you?'

For a second the whole room seemed to quiver out of focus, and Harriet felt herself sway as a sudden weakness claimed her. Grasping the smooth wooden knob on the end of the banister, she held on while his words echoed round and round her head in a sudden surge of pleasure, till slowly sanity returned and swept them away. Marry him...how could she marry him when he was already married?

'Here, sit down before you fall down.'

With an economy of effort Rick swung her round, seating her on the bottom of the stairs while he studied her white face with grim concern. Harriet desperately tried to regather her scattered senses. She had to think, had to try and understand what he was saying, but it was so difficult to think of anything at the moment except those same two tantalising words. Marry him . . . Oh, if only she could! She stared at him, her eyes swimming with tears.

'Rick, I'd marry you tomorrow if I could, but how can I when you're already married?'

There was silence, then he spoke, his voice low and clear, the sweetest words Harriet had ever heard in the whole of her twenty-five years.

'I thought you knew, Harriet; it was in all the papers. My marriage is over and I'm free.'

'Free?' she echoed, then quietly gave in to the faintness.

CHAPTER ELEVEN

THE COFFEE was burning hot and darkly bitter, but to Harriet it tasted like nectar. Sipping at it, she let her eyes travel to Rick who was standing by the stove, his back towards her, and knew that this kitchen had suddenly become a tiny part of heaven.

'All right now?'

Rick crossed the room, pulled out a chair and sat down, his eyes sweeping over her face with a lingering, loving concern.

'Yes, fine,' she whispered. 'But do you think you could explain—everything—from the beginning? This time I promise I really will listen.'

'And about time, too.'

He smiled, a soft, warm smile which chased all the harshness from his face, and Harriet felt her breath catch in her throat. Reaching out, she linked her fingers with his on the table, feeling the faint shudder which raced through him at her touch. Raising her hand, Rick lifted it to his lips, and Harriet felt the brief contact run through her body in an electrifying jolt and stifled a gasp. There was a moment's silence, as though Rick was trying to assemble his thoughts into some sort of order, and then he spoke. Harriet pulled her hand free and sat back in her chair to listen, really listen, to all he could tell her.

'First of all, I'm sorry if I upset you before; it seems to be something I'm exceptionally good at. However, I

174

really and truly thought you'd have read about the divorce in the papers.'

'I haven't. I've been so busy working on the film that I've hardly glanced at a paper in months, and then it was only to read the headlines.'

'I see. Well, it's no wonder it came as a shock and you didn't know what I was talking about,' he said wryly, and she nodded.

'So, when did it all happen, Rick, and why? I mean, was it anything to do with me?'

She stared at him, her face mirroring her concern as she faced the prospect that somehow she might be responsible for breaking up his marriage. It was a harsh thought, and Harriet felt herself go cold to the tips of her toes as she considered it. She wanted Rick, wanted him more than she could ever want anyone else in the whole of her lifetime. He was everything to her, but to gain her happiness at the expense of someone else wasn't something that would set her cheering.

'No, Harriet, you had nothing at all to do with any of it. I was actually divorced the day before I came over to England to stay with Cathy.'

'The day before?' she echoed, her eyes racing to his. 'But, Rick, I don't understand. Are you actually saying that when we met, when we stayed here at the house, before, you weren't married?' Puzzlement showed in her eyes, and he smiled at her a trifle wryly.

'Yes, that's exactly what I'm saying, my love.'

'Then I don't understand. Why didn't you just tell me? Why did you let me go on thinking you were married?'

Hurt bewilderment filled her voice and, reaching across the table, he caught her hand, holding it tight as though terrified she might suddenly turn tail and run.

'I couldn't tell you, Harriet.'

'Couldn't? What do you mean, couldn't?'

'I'd promised Sondra, my ex-wife, that I wouldn't tell anyone at all about the divorce for at least a month. That's why neither the police nor anyone else knew about it.'

'But why? What difference could it make to her?' A raw pain filled her voice, and she felt him flinch, his fingers moving gently against hers.

'Sondra is, or rather was before we were married, an actress. Recently she'd got it into her head to go back to it, and had managed to get an audition for a big part in a new soap opera that's being made very shortly. She begged me not to let the fact that we were getting divorced become public knowledge before the final decision on who was getting the role was made. She had the idea that being my wife might just tip the scales in her favour.'

'And did it?' Harriet asked quietly, her eyes still haunted.

'Oh, yes, definitely. One thing you learn and learn fast in the film business is that it's as much who you know as what you know that gives you the edge over the competition. I can honestly say that her being "my wife" landed her the part, but I'd have never agreed to it if I'd had any inkling just what it would cost me.'

His voice was bitter, and Harriet held his hand tighter, wanting to wipe away some of his pain. Although it still hurt to remember all she'd gone through these past weeks, it was good to know that keeping a promise meant so much to Rick. It took a strong man to do that at the expense of his own happiness; a strong one and a good one.

'I'm sorry, Harriet, really sorry for putting you through all this. When I saw how you looked at me when you thought I was married...well, I'd have given my soul to tell you I wasn't, but I just couldn't. I'd given Sondra my word, and there was no way I could go back on it.'

'I understand, Rick, really,' she said gently, her eyes filled with compassion at his distress. He smiled, the grim, tight lines leaving his face.

'D'you know, I really think you do. You're wonderful, Harriet, have I told you?'

'No, not yet. Still, I'm sure you can make up for such an oversight later,' she said wickedly, and he laughed, his eyes filled with a promise which made her heart leap up and start to hammer hard in her chest. Glancing down, she gave herself a few seconds to get her wayward feelings under control, then prompted gently, 'So, now that's out of the way, Rick, will you tell me about it...your divorce and everything?'

'Yes, of course. I want to tell you, want you to know exactly what happened.'

He was frowning now, his face filled with a bitter sadness, and just for a moment Harriet regretted asking, till slowly it came to her that he needed to talk about all that had gone on in his marriage and eventual divorce as much as she needed to hear. There was no way they could start a new life with the ghost of an old one left to haunt them.

'So what did cause the divorce, Rick? Did you just fall out of love with her, or what?'

It was painful to think of another woman having shared his life, but she knew she had to face it.

'Fall out of love? Hardly,' he said harshly. 'How can you fall out of love when there's been no love there in the first place?'

'No love! But why did you marry her?' Startled, Harriet stared at him.

'Because she was pregnant,' he said baldly, and her face drained of colour. Children! Somehow the thought that he might have children had never occurred to her before, and in a sudden rush she knew there was no way she could grab her own happiness at their expense.

'Sweetheart, are you all right? You've gone so pale!'

Grasping her hand tighter, Rick chafed her cold fingers, but she pulled away, her voice flat, devoid of all the emotion which raged inside her. Suddenly her dreams of happiness seemed to be moving further and further away rather than coming closer. How could he ever make a clean break from his old life when there were children involved? It was hopeless.

'Harriet?'

'I'm...I'm all right, Rick. How many children do you have?' It was an effort to ask, but she knew there was no way she could avoid it.

'None.'

'But you said...'

'I know, I'm sorry—I'm handling this very badly. Let me try again, start from the very beginning.' He ran his fingers through his hair, leaving the golden strands ruffled. 'I met Sondra about four years ago, and we started dating. As I've said, she was an actress, not very well known, but extremely beautiful. Quite frankly, I was very attracted to her physically. Inevitably we had an affair, and as far as I was concerned she knew all the rules; after all, I wasn't the first man she'd been with, far from it! Things had gone on for a few months when gradually I came to realise that while on the outside she might be beautiful, on the inside she was a mess. Vain, grasping, vicious…you name the adjective, and it could describe her. Oh, she tried to hide it, kept it all covered when I was around, but every so often the real side of her came out, till finally I decided I'd had enough and that we might as well finish. That's when she threw her best shot at me. She was pregnant, she said, two months, and what was I going to do about it?'

'So you married her,' Harriet said softly, hating to see the pain which twisted his face.

'Yes, I married her, and it was my biggest mistake.'

'You mean she wasn't pregnant, it was a lie?'

'Oh, no, I wasn't that naïve. She was pregnant all right, I'd seen the medical reports to prove it, but after we'd got married Sondra decided that a baby would be rather too much of an inconvenience in her life. After all, it would put her out of action for several months, might possibly spoil her figure. While I was away on location she had an abortion. She killed the child, Harriet—my child!'

'Oh, Rick!'

There was nothing Harriet could say. The pain was old and obviously deeply entrenched, and there was just no comfort she could offer for it. Taking his hand in hers, she tried some way to communicate all she was feeling, knowing no words could express her horror, and after a few moments he continued, his voice unnaturally flat and level.

'She never told me what she'd done, of course. She knew that would be the end of our relationship. She made up some cock-and-bull story about a miscarriage and how she'd nearly died, etc. Quite impressive really, when one appreciates that she wasn't known for her brilliant acting, and I felt bitterly sorry for her as well as for myself. We drifted on for a couple of years, and after a while I found there was a certain advantage to being married: I could play the field with impunity. After all, I could always turn away from any woman who was getting too demanding with the reminder that I was already married.'

A wealth of scorn and self-disgust laced his voice, but Harriet didn't comment as he looked down at her, knowing there was no way she could presume to stand in judgement on how he'd acted. There had probably been far more to his life, far more hurt and sadness to the tragic marriage, than he'd told her, and with a shrug he continued.

'Sondra started drinking. She'd soon given up the idea of pursuing a career while I could keep her in every luxury, but after a while I think she started getting bored. There was no excitement to life any more, and Sondra is a woman who loves excitement and attention. Anyway, soon the drinking became a problem, an embarrassment to friends and colleagues, and we ended up rowing about it. It was while she was drunk and we were having one of our endless fights that she told me what she'd done: that she'd not miscarried but had got rid of "my brat", as she called it.'

'Oh, Rick, how could she?'

Tears were trickling down Harriet's cheeks now, and he gently brushed them away, his eyes sad.

'I don't know, honey, I really don't. After that—well, there was just nothing left and divorce was inevitable. In a way I think the shock of reaching that point did her good; it certainly sobered her up and set her thinking what to do with her life. That's when she decided to go back to acting. She soon landed a few small parts in different television serials, then along came the proposal for the new "soap", and she decided to audition for it. I was only too pleased to keep the plans for the divorce quiet as there was no way I wanted our private life pulled apart for public inspection, so I agreed to her pleas and promised I'd not let news of it leak out till after they'd decided on who'd got the role. God, if only I'd known what it would mean when I made that promise!'

His voice was filled with a wry sadness, and Harriet smiled gently at him, her eyes filled with love for this man who'd faced so much unhappiness in his life.

'Anyway, the divorce hearing was very quick and the settlement date was made for a month later, which suited us both fine. I'd just finished work on a film and knew that I needed to get away, get everything back into perspective. I'd been drifting far too long, but now the relationship with Sondra was over it was time I made a few decisions about where I was going. I decided to come over to England and spend a couple of weeks with Cathy just to get some breathing space and sort things out in my head, and that's when I met you...and you, Harriet, bowled me over!'

'I did?' Blushing, Harriet looked down at their linked hands, hearing him chuckle softly at her sudden confusion.

'You certainly did. I'd never met a woman like you before; you were so full of spunk, so sparky and so utterly determined not to like me that I knew I just had to change your mind. You must believe me when I say that I never meant to deceive you in any way at all, it was just that everything happened so fast. I knew I was falling in love with you and that I must explain about my marriage and everything, but I couldn't. I couldn't break my word, no matter how much I wanted to. The trouble was, we just didn't have enough time together, did we, my love? Just those two brief days, then it was all over.'

'No,' she answered quietly, 'no, we never had the time then, but we do have it now.' She stared into his eyes, her own dark and deep with emotion, and said softly, 'I love you, Rick. I loved you then and I still love you now. I was just afraid to face it before.'

'Oh, Harriet, you don't know how much I've ached to hear you say that!'

For a moment tears clouded the green of his eyes, and he glanced away, his voice suddenly rough with emotion as he carried on with his tale.

'After you'd returned home I went to London and had a meeting with Sondra to find out what she thought she was doing following me over here, and that was the biggest mistake I could ever have made. I must have been more upset about the way we'd parted than I realised, for somehow I let slip about us being stranded here together and it was just the opening she needed. She'd done her homework, all right, found out from poor unsuspecting Cathy about the camp and who was going on it, then when I mentioned your name she put two and two together. She threatened to leak to the Press that you'd been the cause of our break-up, unless I added another clause to the divorce settlement.'

'How awful! Why on earth didn't you contact me? I would have denied everything, of course. After all, nothing happened between us, and by the time we met you weren't even married to her.'

'I know, but mud sticks, and there was no way I could take a chance on your getting hurt any more than you were already. And if nothing happened, as you put it, it wasn't for want of trying. In my mind I made love to you a hundred times over during those two days!'

'Rick Dawson, you were supposed to be sick!'

'Sick with frustration more likely, my love. How I kept my hands off you, I don't know; I must have had an awful lot of will-power! Anyway, if you remember I did try to talk with you the day after we left here, but you wouldn't listen and I still wasn't able to fully explain the situation.'

'I couldn't listen, Rick,' she said, her voice full of remembered pain. 'I felt as though the whole world had just fallen round my shoulders, and that if I weakened I'd be crushed to dust. Deep down I knew I loved you and it terrified me, not only because I believed that you were already married, but because suddenly you'd turned out to be someone else, someone very important, not just Rick. Why didn't you tell me who you were, Rick? Why did you let me believe you were just an actor?'

He shrugged. 'I don't know, really. Maybe it was because I wanted you to love me for myself, for the person I am, not because I'm James Merrick Dawson, and all that his money stands for.'

'Rick, I wouldn't care if you were penniless. In fact, I'd rather you weren't so rich. All that money makes me feel uncomfortable, somehow.'

'Well, maybe what's happened has been for the best, after all,' he said wryly, and Harriet stared at him, puzzled.

'What do you mean?'

'Well, Sondra's reason for following me over was quite simple ... money. It had been whispered to her that her bid for the part would be viewed even more favourably if I decided to put some cash into the venture. Then, when she suddenly found she had this unexpected hold over me, she decided that she might as well guarantee her success with a larger investment to the tune of well over half my bank balance! I couldn't even call her bluff and threaten to make the divorce public knowledge, because if I did then she would go straight to the Press with her lies about you.'

'Oh, Rick, you shouldn't have done it. I'd have managed...somehow.' There was little conviction to her voice, and he smiled, his eyes suddenly tender as they studied her anxious face.

'Oh, no, you wouldn't, Harriet. You would have hated it, and maybe even worse, have ended up hating me for letting it all happen. Sondra could make Snow White look black if she set her mind to it, and there was no way I was going to let her put you through all that. No, I don't give a damn about the money, it's replaceable, but you're not.'

There was so much arrogant conviction in his voice that Harriet laughed, the sound rippling round the quiet kitchen. Looking at her, Rick smiled too, the grimness leaving his face.

'After it was all finally settled, then I knew it was time to come back to England, and I found myself drawn to this house as if to a magnet. After all, it was the one place we'd been together, so to my mind it was very important. I made some enquiries and found out that the last owner had died about six months previously, and that now her will had been through probate there were plans to put it on to the market. She was an artist, strangely enough; she painted those watercolours in the hall and that one over there. Somehow, when I found that out it made everything doubly appropriate, as though the house was meant for you and that you'd be happy here.'

'I knew I felt comfortable here,' she murmured, looking at the small, delicate watercolour of the river hanging on the far wall, 'and now I know why. It must have been her materials I used to draw with when I was here.'

'Yes, I found bits and pieces of stuff all over the place when I took it over. I found that pad you'd been using, too, and that's when I had the idea of getting you to work for me. I loved your cartoon, knew that it was just what Jason was looking for, and knew too that it could serve another purpose. If you were working for me, then I'd be able to keep track of you, know you were safe, that you'd...that you'd not met anyone else. That really ate into me, Harriet, the thought that you might meet another guy and fall for him. I don't think I could have handled that.'

There was raw pain in his voice, and Harriet gripped his hand hard in both of hers, her voice filled with conviction when she spoke.

'I could never have met anyone else, Rick. I was in love with you even though I wouldn't admit it. Oh, to be honest I tried, tried to feel something for Jason, but I couldn't. You'd claimed my heart and it was no longer mine to give.'

'Thank heavens,' he whispered, his voice aching with the pain he'd felt. 'I kept in constant touch with Fane, pretending it was the film I was interested in, while all the time it was just you I wanted to hear about, and gradually I started to realise that he was getting more involved with you than I'd planned on. There was a note to his voice when he spoke your name which made my hackles rise, and I knew I had to come back, had to see you, although deep down I was afraid it was too soon.

I couldn't take the chance that you might fall in love with him instead of me.'

'There was never any chance of that, Rick,' she said softly.

'No? I hope not.'

Rick came round the table and slowly drew her to her feet, his arms encircling her body to pull her against the hard, firm length of his. He stared into her eyes for one long moment, then said quietly, 'I'll never let you go now, Harriet, so will you marry me and live here with me?'

Harriet smiled gently at him, all the love she felt showing in her eyes.

'Yes, Rick. Oh, yes, please.'

Then she waited for him to kiss her.

Dawn was breaking, a dull, grey, rain-soaked dawn, and Harriet chuckled softly. With a bit of luck and a lot of water, maybe they'd find themselves marooned here once again; one could only hope!

Pushing back the bedclothes, she slid from the bed, moving carefully so she wouldn't wake Rick, who was quietly sleeping. She pulled the blankets back over his bare shoulders and stared down at him for a few moments, the happiness welling in her heart rising up and threatening to spill over. She loved him so much, it was almost impossible to put it into words.

Turning away from the bed, she walked softly to the window and, pushing back the silky new curtains, stared out across the flat green sweep of land down to the river. All around the countryside was still, filled only with the muted sounds of nature and little sound of man; the perfect place to live and build their life. Obviously Rick's business interests meant he would have to return to the

States many times a year, but this house in this quiet setting would be their home base, and the thought filled her with pleasure.

Hugging her arms round her body, Harriet let her mind drift back to the hours they'd just spent together and knew that nothing could ever have prepared her for such a rage of feeling which they'd shared. Colour flooded her face, warmth encased her body, and she rested her forehead against the cold glass of the window as her mind stole back over the beauty of their lovemaking.

Rick had been so gentle, so tender and caring, determined to make it as wonderful for her this first time as he could. And it *had* been wonderful, more wonderful than she could ever have imagined. Slowly, unselfishly, he'd aroused her to passion, keeping an iron rein on his own feelings so that by the time they'd become one she'd felt little discomfort, just a sense of deep completeness, followed by ecstasy as the whole world started to spin. Just remembering it now made her breasts ache and her stomach clench in sudden longing.

'Are you all right?'

Rick's voice broke the spell of memory which held her, and she turned to smile at him, her face alight, made beautiful with happiness, so that for a moment it stole his breath and stunned his mind.

'I'm fine. I was just thinking . . . about how wonderful it all is.'

Crossing the room, she slid back into the bed, snuggling her cold body against the warmth of his, her fingers lightly tracing over his bare chest and down to rest on the faint, puckered skin on his side, a souvenir of his accident with the log. She'd been so upset to see it last night, to see the beautiful smooth flesh marred in that way, but he'd pulled her to him, his eyes deep green as he'd told her that any amount of scars were unimportant as long as she was safe. Remembering it now made her feel even more loved and cared for, and she smiled.

Rick moved, sliding his body down to pull her tighter against him, then gently smoothing the tangled auburn hair from off her face. Slowly his fingers traced a gentle path over the curve of her cheek down to her lips, and lingered on them in a caress which made the ache inside her flare to sudden, brilliant life. Breathlessly she pressed herself closer, her fingers moving round to the silken skin of his back, and she smiled when she felt him shudder.

'So you can make me tremble and you think it's funny, do you?'

With a mock growl Rick tilted her chin and stared down into her face, his eyes sparkling with amusement and something else, something which made a quiver race through her. Then suddenly all the laughter left his face as he said slowly, 'I love you, Harriet, but are you sure, really sure that you love me...that there'll never be anyone else?'

There was a need for reassurance in his deep, soft voice, and Harriet smiled, the warm, tender smile of a woman holding the man she loves in her arms. Leaning forwards, her lips just a hair's breadth away from his, she whispered softly, 'I love you, Rick, just you. You'll always be the first, last and only man on earth I'll ever love.'

And gently she kissed him.

BETRAYALS, DECISIONS AND CHOICES...

BUY OUT by David Wind   £2.95

The money-making trend of redeveloping Manhattan tenement blocks
sets the scene for this explosive novel. In the face of shady deals and
corrupt landlords, tenants of the Crestfield begin a fight for their
rights – and end up in a fight for their lives.

BEGINNINGS by Judith Duncan   £2.50

Judith Duncan, bestselling author of "Into the Light", blends sensitivity
and insight in this novel of a woman determined to make a new
beginning for herself and her children. But an unforeseen problem
arises with the arrival of Grady O'Neil.

ROOM FOR ONE MORE by Virginia Nielsen   £2.75

At 38, Charlotte Emlyn was about to marry Brock Morley – 5 years
her junior. Then her teenage son announced that his girlfriend was
pregnant. Could Brock face being husband, stepfather *and* grandfather
at 33? Suddenly 5 years seemed like a lifetime – but could the
dilemma be overcome?.

**These three new titles will be out in bookshops from
MAY 1989**

W●RLDWIDE

*Available from Boots, Martins, John Menzies, W.H. Smith, Woolworths
and other paperback stockists.*

AROUND THE WORLD WORDSEARCH
COMPETITION!

How would you like a years supply of Mills & Boon Romances ABSOLUTELY FREE? Well, you can win them! All you have to do is complete the word puzzle below and send it in to us by October 31st. 1989. The first 5 correct entries picked out of the bag after that date will win **a years supply of Mills & Boon Romances** (*ten books every month - **worth around £150**) What could be easier?

```
R D N A L R E Z T I W S
E O N M C H I N A A C C
G M U I G L E B N N U O
Y E C E G W H I Z C B T
P D R H S E R I A Z A L
T N S M P E R U N D D A
N A W I A T P I I E N N
Y L A T I N A N A N A D
N G S T N H Y D E M L Q
W N O J A M A I C A L A
R E L A D A N A C R O R
T H A I L A N D D K H I
```

ITALY	THAILAND	SCOTLAND	SWITZERLAND
GERMANY	IRAQ	JAMAICA	
HOLLAND	ZAIRE	TANZANIA	
BELGIUM	TAIWAN	PERU	
EGYPT	CANADA	SPAIN	
CHINA	INDIA	DENMARK	
NIGERIA	ENGLAND	CUBA	

PLEASE TURN OVER FOR DETAILS ON HOW TO ENTER

HOW TO ENTER

All the words listed overleaf, below the word puzzle, are hidden in the grid. You can find them by reading the letters forward, backwards, up or down, or diagonally. When you find a word, circle it or put a line through it, the remaining letters (which you can read from left to right, from the top of the puzzle through to the bottom) will spell a secret message.

After you have filled in all the words, don't forget to fill in your name and address in the space provided and pop this page in an envelope (you don't need a stamp) and post it today. Hurry - competition ends October 31st. 1989.

Mills & Boon Competition,
FREEPOST,
P.O. Box 236,
Croydon,
Surrey. CR9 9EL

Only one entry per household

Secret Message _____

_____

Name _____

Address _____

_____

_____

_____ Postcode _____

You may be mailed as a result of entering this competition